ROTHIEMURCHUS

Other books of similar interest from Scottish Cultural Press

From the Institute for Environmental History

Fragile Environments *G Whittington (ed)*   1 898218 77 5
The History of Souls and Field Systems *S Foster & T C Smout (eds)* 1 898218 13 7
Scotland Since Prehistory *T C Smout (ed)* 1 898218 03 X
Scottish Woodland History   *T C Smout (ed)* 1 898218 53 6
Species History in Scotland *R A Lambert (ed)* 1 84017 011 5

From the Scottish Wildlife Trust

The Nature of Fife [includes species listings] *G B Corbet (ed)* 1 84017 008 5

Associated interest

The Cairngorm Gateway *A Glen*   1 84017 027 1
Capable Citizens and Improvident Democrats [A concise account of the Scottish electoral system
      1884-1929]   *M Dyer* 1 898218 23 4
Discover Scotland's History *A D Cameron*   1 898218 76 5
Edinburgh 'a la carte'– the history of food in Edinburgh *M Turnbull*   1 898218 87 0
Men of Property and Intelligence [A concise account of the Scottish electoral system prior to
      1884]   *M Dyer* 1 898218 22 6
Moray Firth Ships and Trade in the 19th century *I Hustwick*   1 898218 05 6
Parish Life in 18th century Scotland *M Steven* 1 898218 28 5
Pine Trees and the Sky – life in a Highland glen *J Cantlie Stewart* 1 898218 97 8
Scotland's Rural Land Use Agencies *D G Mackay* 1 898218 31 5
Scottish Lifestyle 300 years ago *K & H Kelsall*   1 898218 05 4
The Uses of Place-Names *S Taylor (ed)* 1 8988218 98 6

ROTHIEMURCHUS

Nature and People
on a Highland Estate
1500–2000

T C Smout & R A Lambert (eds)

SCOTTISH CULTURAL PRESS

First published 1999

Scottish Cultural Press
Unit 13d
Newbattle Abbey College Business Annexe
Newbattle Road
DALKEITH
EH22 3LJ

Tel: 0131 660 6366
Fax: 0131 660 6414
e-mail: scp@sol.co.uk

ISBN: 1 84017 033 6

Printed and bound by Cromwell Press Ltd, Trowbridge, Wiltshire

Contents

List of black and white illustrations

Foreword

Magnus Magnusson KBE

> I was born on the 7th of May, 1797, of a Sunday evening at No 5 (north side)
> of Charlotte Square, Edinburgh, in my father's own lately built house, and I
> am the eldest of the five children he and my Mother reared to maturity. My
> parents had married young. My father wanted a few weeks of 22 and my
> Mother a few of 21 when they went together for better, for worse, my poor
> Mother!

That is how Elizabeth Grant of Rothiemurchus opened her remarkable life-story,
The Memoirs of a Highland Lady. Her tale was first published one hundred years
ago and has been an unlikely best-seller ever since. On the bicentenary of her
birth, the conference which inspired this book was designed to celebrate and
illuminate that multi-faceted world of Rothiemurchus, both past and present,
which Elizabeth Grant did so much to immortalise:

> It was in July or August 1803 when we crossed the Spey in the big boat at
> Inverdruie in a perfect fever of happiness. Every mountain, every hill, every
> bank, fence, path, tree, cottage was known to us, every face we met revealed a
> friend's, and our acquaintance was by no means limited; for the 'wide plain of
> fir trees', which lies in the bosom of the Grampians, cut off by the rapid Spey
> from every neighbour, has its beautiful variety of mountain scenery, its
> heights and dells and glens, its lakes and plains and haughs, and its miles and
> miles of dark pine forest through which were little clearings by the side of the
> rapid burnies, and here and there a sawmill. We were expected, so from the
> boathouse to The Doune it was one long gathering, all our people flocking to
> meet us and to shout the 'Welcome home!

Rothiemurchus, the real gateway to Elizabeth's life, and the gateway to the
Cairngorms, has become a name which is etched deep in the consciousness of
Scotland and which holds an exceptional place in the natural history of Scotland.

I first came across Rothiemurchus as a young journalist quartering the
Highlands and Islands for the *Scottish Daily Express*. That was in the days when
Colonel John P Grant, Johnny's father, was the laird of Rothiemurchus, and
rumour had it that he cruised around his estates in a Landrover with a shotgun on
his knees, looking for stray tourists to cull. It was not long after the disastrous
picnic fire which destroyed so much of the woodland, and whose scars can still
be seen, so perhaps there was some excuse for his wrath.

What change there has been! For more than 20 years his son Johnny Grant,
along with his wife Philippa, has toiled to develop Rothiemurchus from a

traditional Highland estate to the present operation, which involves about 50 staff working in a complex, multiple land-use business. Today Rothiemurchus has become an icon of enlightened conservation management far furth of the borders of Scotland. The visitor-culling policy of Colonel J P has been transformed, and Rothiemurchus now welcomes around 300,000 visitors a year, and is the first estate in Britain to have achieved 'Investors in People' standard. Where before it was a choice between Nature *or* People, today Rothiemurchus is, as the title of the Conference underlined, a happy and harmonious marriage of Nature *and* People.

Over the last 20 years, too, the Grants have restored the historic mansion of The Doune, the home which Elizabeth Grant of Rothiemurchus described so fondly in *Memoirs of a Highland Lady*. The Doune has been rescued from ruin after an undignified descent to a hotel and a rented shooting lodge and, now that the Grants have moved in, there is life and youthful laughter again in the venerable old house.

I think we can regard Rothiemurchus as a Highland parable of our modern times. The extraordinarily strong feelings which Elizabeth Grant had for Rothiemurchus – an exclusive and privileged love of its countryside – can now be shared by the people of Scotland as a whole.

What this century has seen is what one could call the democratisation of the 'Rothiemurchus feeling'. Rothiemurchus is no longer the preserve of the élite. Anyone and everyone can go there and enjoy it: it's *our* beloved Rothiemurchus now. Elizabeth Grant, I hope, would have approved.

Introduction

The notion for this book emerged during one evening of pleasant hospitality at the Doune, where both editors have enjoyed the privilege of working on their own separate research topics in the archives stored in the attics. John and Philippa Grant gave it their warm support. The various authors we approached were enthusiastic, and at the subsequent two-day conference – one hearing the papers at the Royal College of Physicians in Edinburgh, and one walking the land on Rothiemurchus itself – we all gained a great deal from interactions between the speakers and those who attended. The result is in some respects different from the papers given in Edinburgh – the papers generally are longer and more considered – but the purpose is the same: to record and celebrate the history of over 400 years of management of Rothiemurchus by one family, on the occasion of Elizabeth Grant's bicentenary.

It is not a tale without its ups and downs, and it encompasses the built heritage as well as the natural heritage. The lairds have been both good and bad, and all of them (like all of us) a mixture of both: it would have been disrespectful to the memory of that most candid of family chroniclers, Elizabeth Grant herself, not to have told the story warts and all. In these days of proposed land reform, however, it is worth putting on record the contribution that continuity of management has undoubtedly made to conservation on this estate. The lands of Rothiemurchus would surely not still be so fine for the pleasure of the entire people of Scotland had not the ideal of stewardship (however interpreted) been real for the Grant lairds over several generations.

Thanks are due to John and Philippa Grant first, then to Chloë Randall and Margaret Richards, who respectively at Rothiemurchus and at St Andrews, made the proposed conference a reality. The Cairngorms Partnership Board, the Royal Commission on the Ancient and Historic Monuments of Scotland and Scottish Natural Heritage provided financial assistance towards publication, for which we are most grateful. To all who came to the conference and the field trips we express our thanks for their good fellowship, interest and encouragement.

Robert A Lambert,
Chris Smout
Institute for Environmental History
University of St Andrews

1. The Background to Medieval Rothiemurchus

G W S Barrow

The thanage or thanedom of Rothiemurchus,[1] some 36,000 acres and including the summit of the third highest mountain in Britain, has two features in particular pointing to some degree of antiquity as a human settlement. The name itself takes us back to the period, in the eighth and ninth centuries, when the Gaelic-speaking Scots from Dalriada were asserting supremacy over the Pictish population of northern and eastern Scotland and making sure they slept soundly at night by building fortified settlements for which the word *rath* was used.[2] We know nothing of Muirgus or Morcus whose *rath* this was; if the Doune marks its site, it was presumably chosen because this is the narrowest point in the valley of the Spey between its source and the sea.

The second early feature is the dedication of the church to Saint Duchaldus.[3] The name is meaningless as it stands, but if as seems probable it represents do-Cheallaich[4] that would point to one of the two Cellachs abbots of Iona or – this seems most likely in my view – the Cellach who went to Northumbria with Aedán and Finán, was briefly bishop among the Mercians after the fall of King Penda, and in the later 650s retired to Iona to exercise episcopal functions among his fellow Scots. The Scottish saints advanced into Badenoch and Strathspey along with or even in advance of the Scottish war-lords:[5] Kenneth of Aghabo at Laggan, Columcille at Kingussie, Adamnán at Insh, Tommaltach at Kincardine, Molúoc of Lismore at Raitts, Brigid or Bride – well, one of the fifteen Brigids – at Glen Banchor west of Newtonmore. Cellach would sit comfortably in this company.

When we first hear of Rothiemurchus, in 1226, it was in the hands of the Crown and was being granted by way of excambion or exchange to Andrew Murray, bishop of Moray and chief builder of the beautiful cathedral of the Holy Trinity at Elgin.[6] It seems, at first sight, a rather strange gift: Rothiemurchus, to be held by the bishop of the crown in forest, with the standard penalty of £10 sterling for anyone cutting down trees or hunting without the bishop's leave. Of course, the bishop and his household would engage in hunting, but if they were to enjoy their sport in Rothiemurchus they would need houses and stabling, kitchens and larders.

Place-names and physical survivals clearly demonstrate that coniferous trees – specifically the Scots fir, *pinus silvestris* – grew at an appreciably greater height above sea-level within the historical period. Up in Glen Einich there are 'allt a' phrisghiubhais' and 'càrn a' phrisghiubhais',[7] respectively burn and hill of the fir woodie, and most famously of course, there is Glen Geusachan,[8] 'glen of the pine wood', over the other side of the hills and running down into Glen Dee. There are still abundant remains of old pine tree roots and stumps in the bogs of Glen Geusachan, between 1,700 and 2,000 feet. Rothiemurchus was – as it still is – part of a well-wooded region of Scotland.

The particular value of a base at Rothiemurchus for the bishop of Moray lay in the fact that his see and cathedral church were endowed with several parish kirks and the lands attached to them in Badenoch – Laggan, Kingussie with its chapels, Insh and the chapel of Dunachton. A sojourn in Rothiemurchus would provide a convenient opportunity for the bishop to visit his flock, bring wrongdoers to justice and receive the homage of his vassals and tenants. Considerations of this sort make particularly attractive the suggestion of Ian Bryce that the earliest element in the complex we know as Loch an Eilein Castle – namely the hall-house occupying the south end of the built area – was the work of Bishop Andrew between 1222 and 1242.[9] It might, alternatively, have been constructed for Bishop Andrew's successor and possible kinsman Bishop Archibald. But Archibald's episcopate, though long (1253–98), has left strangely little in the way of record, and we have no notion of how often he visited the highland parts of his diocese.[10]

Since Rothiemurchus constituted a thanage, either immemorially royal or royal since the forfeiture of Angus, last mormaer of Moray in 1130, the bishops would be served by a resident thane, holding office heritably. Here we come up against the serious problem of lack of documentation. In the fifteenth century there is no doubt that the office of thane of Rothiemurchus was held by Alasdair *Ciar* Macintosh (Alasdair the 'swarthy'),[11] a close kinsman of Malcolm Macintosh and his son Duncan, who were vassals of the lords of the Isles in Lochaber.[12] Since the lineage name *mac an tóiseaich* means 'son of the thane', it seems reasonable to suppose that the lineage name was derived from the office of thane of Rothiemurchus.

No thane as such is on record before the fifteenth century, and no Macintosh is on record before the 1330s. Nevertheless, the tradition that the Rothiemurchus family adopted as a species of lineage name the personal name Sídheach ('wolf') – rendered in Latin documents as Old Testament Seth and englished as Shaw – is too well-documented and circumstantial to be dismissed.[13] The name Sídheach takes us back to the thirteenth century, when Ferchar son of Sídheach was steward of the lordship of Badenoch and had a manor-house on the hillock (*stúcan*) of Dalnavert.[14] Although this was only a few miles from Rothiemurchus there is nothing to connect Ferchar with the thanage save for the name Sídheach or Shaw.

There is evidence that towards the end of the fourteenth century the bishop of Moray could no longer rely on a hereditary thane to manage Rothiemurchus and defend it against robbers and caterans. In 1370 Alexander Stewart, a younger son of the seventh hereditary Stewart of Scotland (soon to be King Robert II) – notorious in later history as the 'Wolf of Badenoch' – declared in a solemn document issued at his castle of Ruthven by Kingussie that he had become the defender and protector of the men and lands of Alexander Bur bishop of Moray within the parts of Strathspey and Badenoch.[15] He would cherish them as though they were his own and would never bring them into his courts or judgements, nor would he ever demand any duties on animal skins, or levies of corn, cattle or marts. Since he had no seal, he had arranged for his father's seal to be fixed to the document.

Thirteen years later Bishop Bur gave Alexander, by now earl of Buchan as well as lord of Badenoch, a tack for three lives of the whole of Rothiemurchus, reckoned to be six davochs, to be held in free forest.[16] The bishop proposed to take a high annual ferme of £8 sterling, doubled for Stewart's heirs after his death. In return, Stewart undertook to see that the land was tenanted and managed and, in addition, he would protect the bishop's lands of Finlargs in Strathspey from evildoers.

Despite the privilege of 'free forest' the bishop was careful to reserve to himself and future bishops all nests or eyries of hawks, as often as hawks may build their nests. Moreover, Stewart and his heirs were to protect and conserve all the nests which hawks might build for the duration of the tack, and they were to protect all the woodland and not sell or give away or in any way exploit any of the woods without the bishop's leave, save only what was needed to erect and repair buildings, and necessities for the people living on the estate.

Hereditary thanedoms were not easily extinguished. It is surely significant that in granting the tack to the king's brother, powerful and (as time would sadly prove) dangerous though he was, the bishop carefully provided that Alexander would not obstruct anyone who might claim the estate by hereditary right, nor must he obstruct the bishop if he wished to do justice to such a person. Relations between Bishop Bur and Alexander Stewart grew steadily worse, until in 1389 the bishop dismissed Stewart as protector of his see and appointed Thomas Dunbar, eldest son of the earl of Moray.[17] Two months after Robert II's death and two months before the crowning of Robert III, on 17 June 1390, Alexander Stewart descended on Forres and Elgin with a force of the very caterans and malefactors against whom he was supposed to protect the church and clergy of Moray. The two royal burghs were sacked and burned, and in Elgin not only were the parish kirk and the Maison Dieu hospital destroyed, along with eighteen houses of the canons, but the very cathedral itself, the finest gothic building in northern Scotland, was consigned to the flames.[18]

The sack of Elgin, for which the Wolf of Badenoch was never punished, did not put a stop to the episcopal policy of trying to find a powerful noble to act as protector of the church. At different times the earls of Moray and Huntly and the lords of the Isles were required to perform this defensive role. Rothiemurchus, however, was not again set in tack to one of the magnates, but seems to have reverted to its thanes, Macintoshes *alias* Shaws. In 1464 Bishop David Stewart issued a feu-ferme charter (the standard tenure for thanages) to Alexander Ciar Macintosh, who was to pay the bishop 24 merks a year till he could provide lands for the bishop in the Laich of Moray.[19] The formal reddendo, interestingly, was one fir cone annually if requested.

In the sixteenth century, Alasdair Ciar's grandson, Alan Ciar Macintosh, got into financial difficulties and in 1539 sold the liferent of Rothiemurchus to Master George Gordon, constable of Ruthven – explicitly including the loch and castle.[20] By this time, exploitation of the woodland was perhaps beginning to catch up with conservation in the episcopal 'barony of Spynie', of which Rothiemurchus had formed a constituent element since James II's grant in 1451 to his friend and strong supporter bishop John Winchester.[21] We learn that Gordon will make available to the bishop every year, as his Macintosh predecessors have been accustomed to do, 160 fir tree trunks big enough to serve as joists. This timber was to be delivered at the bank of the Spey beneath Rothiemurchus kirk, stacked on a space big enough to allow the logs to be pitched into the river in a float or in some other way as may be thought speedful.[22]

1.1: The stronghold of Rothiemurchus – Loch an Eilein Castle (13th–15th century?)
Photograph: J E A Steggall, April 1922, Neg. 40.2.
By kind permission of the University of St Andrews Photographic Collection.

It is to the period of the revived thanedom, in the middle of the fifteenth century, that Ian Bryce would assign the construction of the sturdy tower-house element of Loch an Eilein castle, 10 m long by 8½ m broad, with walls six feet (1.8 m) thick, a barrel-vaulted cellar, first floor hall and upper chamber.[23] If castle building does not seem to have been a typical thanely activity in the twelfth or thirteenth centuries, Cawdor Castle's oldest element is enough to show that thanes could and did build tower-houses in the fifteenth century.[24] But, with little or none of Mr Bryce's expertise in the field of military architecture, I cannot see any insuperable obstacle to attributing the tower part of Loch an Eilein castle to the Wolf of Badenoch in the 1380s. He would certainly have had the resources and manpower to build himself a fortified hunting lodge, conveniently placed between Ruthven and Lochindorb. The Macintosh thanes, on the other hand, might have been expected to reside at the Doune and build there.

Rothiemurchus, then, was a busy place in the medieval period, and – despite seeming to be tucked away and remote – an important place, much in the minds of kings, bishops and powerful lords. Under the bishops of Moray and after their time it formed a *dùthchas* which Macintosh, understandably, bitterly regretted losing and which Patrick Grant of Muckrach, understandably, must have been eager to acquire.

Notes

1. Rothiemurchus is not called a thanage in documents of the thirteenth or fourteenth century, although references to thanages are by no means uncommon in Moray sources of that period. But in a bond of manrent of 1472 Alexander Macintosh is styled thane of 'Rathamurcus' (*Miscellany of the Spalding Club*, ii (1842), 252).

2. For the formation of place-names in *rath* in central and eastern Scotland, see W.J. Watson, *History of the Celtic Place-Names of Scotland* (Edinburgh, 1926), 237-9; see also p.517. *Rath* is a comparatively rare place-name element in the west of Scotland, Rahoy in Morvern being one example.

3. J.M. Mackinlay, *Ancient Church Dedications in Scotland: Non-Scriptural Dedications* (1914), 505. According to Mackinlay, Duchaldus was traditionally connected with Iona; his information apparently came from the minister of Rothiemurchus, the Rev. D. McDougall.

4. i.e. Cellach or Ceollach prefixed by the affectionate possessive pronoun *do*, 'thy', an occasional alternative to *mo* 'my'. There is a not very helpful mention of a saint Mocheallog in Mackinlay, op. cit., p. 138. For the abbots of Iona called Cellach, see *Life of St Columba*, ed. W. Reeves (Edinburgh, 1874), pp. clxxiv-clxxv. Bede gives some particulars of Cellach (Ceollach), bishop among the Mercians and Middle Angles: *Venerabilis Baedae Opera Historica*, ed. C. Plummer (Oxford, 1896, reprinted 1946, 1956), I, pp. 171, 179. For a general review of the evidence for Iona-related saints in eastern Scotland see S. Taylor, 'Seventh-century Iona abbots in Scottish place-names', *Innes Review*, 48 (1997), 45-72.

5. The earliest known saints who were titulars of churches and chapels of Badenoch and upper Strathspey are dealt with in the works of Mackinlay and Watson already mentioned. See also G.W.S.Barrow, 'Badenoch and Strathspey, 1130-1312, 2: The Church', *Northern Scotland*, 9 (1989), 1-16.

6. *Registrum Episcopatus Moraviensis* (Edinburgh, Bannatyne Club, 1837 [hereafter *Moray Reg.*], no. 29 (31 March, 1226).

7.   NG Ref NH 9303.

8.   NG Ref NN 9694.

9.   Ian B.D. Bryce, 'Loch an Eilein Castle, Rothiemurchus', *Aberdeen University Review*, no. 186 (1991), 138, 141.

10.   J. Dowden, *The Bishops of Scotland* (Edinburgh, 1912) [hereafter Dowden, *Bishops*], 150-1, brings together most of what is known of Bishop Archibald, although his statement that 'charter evidence is abundant' (p. 150) was surely meant to apply to Bishop Andrew, not Archibald.

11.   Above, n. 1; *Moray Reg.*, no. 448. The by-name Keir of the document represents Gaelic *ciar*, 'swarthy'. It was used by Alasdair's descendants.

12.   *Acts of the Lords of the Isles, 1336-1493*, ed. J. and R.W. Munro (Edinburgh, Scottish History Society, 1986), p. xxxi and nos. 4, 62-64, 88; A.M. Mackintosh, *The Mackintoshes and Clan Chattan* (Edinburgh, 1903), 88. I have to thank Dr Jean Munro for kindly helping me with details of Mackintosh/Shaw history.

13.   G.F. Black, *The Surnames of Scotland* (New York, 1946), 721 ('Shaw' no. 2); A.M. Mackintosh (or Shaw), *The Mackintoshes*, 58, 405-414. Little light is thrown on the link between Mackintosh and Shaw by *The Mackintosh Muniments, 1442-1820*, ed. H. Paton (Edinburgh, privately printed, 1903).

14.   *Moray Reg.*, no. 85, 86 (1234); *Miscellany of the Spalding Club*, iv (1849), 125.

15.   *Moray Reg*, no. 154. Alexander was given the lordship of Badenoch by his father in 1371 (ibid., pp. 472-3).

16.   *Moray Reg.*, no. 162.

17.   *Moray Reg.*, no. 170. A detailed account of the relations between Bishop Bur and Alexander Stewart is given by Dr Alexander Grant in *Moray: province and people*, ed. W.D.H. Sellar (Scottish Society for Northern Studies, Edinburgh, 1993), 'The Wolf of Badenoch', pp. 143-161. Dr Grant accepts the contemporary verdict of parliament on the Wolf, that he was 'of no use to the community'.

18.   R. Nicholson, *Scotland: the Later Middle Ages* (Edinburgh, 1974), 205. But evidently the cathedral was badly dilapidated by the 1360s: Dowden, *Bishops*, 155.

19.   *Moray Reg.*, no. 448. Relationship between Duncan chief of Mackintosh and Alexander (Alasdair) Ciar is implied by *Mackintosh Muniments*, no. 10 and W. Fraser, *The Chiefs of Grant* (Edinburgh, 1883), iii, p. 363 (1475-6).

20.   *Moray Reg.*, no. 449 (November 1539-January 1540).

21.   *Moray Reg.*, no. 193.

22.   *Moray Reg.*, no. 449.

23.   Bryce, 'Loch an Eilein Castle' (as above, no. 9), 138, 141.

24.   D. MacGibbon and T. Ross, *The Castellated and Domestic Architecture of Scotland* (reprint edn, Edinburgh, 1971), ii, 315-6.

2. The Gaelic Heritage of Rothiemurchus

James H Grant

Although many people today do not readily associate the Gaelic language with Rothiemurchus, for over a thousand years Gaelic was the principal language spoken in the area. As recently as the 1901 Census, 56% of the population of Rothiemurchus are recorded as being Gaelic speaking and one of these is recorded as being 'Gaelic only'. Today the situation is very different, for there are now no native speakers of the local Strathspey dialect of Gaelic resident in Rothiemurchus.

At one time everyone, including the laird, spoke Gaelic and participated fully in all aspects of Gaelic culture. At least one of the present laird's ancestors was a competent Gaelic poet – this was James, the fifth Laird, who was born c.1692 and died in 1768. Only one of his pieces of poetry survives, *Oran Bròin air Tighearna Ghrannda*, composed in 1719 (Grannd 1986: 39–43).

One of the two principal Gaelic poets of the 1745 Rising, Colonel John Roy Stuart, had strong Rothiemurchus connections. He was born in 1700 in Kincardine, just three miles to the east of Rothiemurchus, his mother came from Giuslich in Rothiemurchus and he composed poetry to the Grant family of Rothiemurchus. During the Rising he commanded the Edinburgh Regiment which contained not only men from Edinburgh and other districts, but his relatives and friends from Strathspey. After Culloden, he spent some months hiding in various locations within Rothiemurchus and other parts of Strathspey. He then fled into exile in France along with Prince Charles in September 1746. Much of his poetry can be found in Thomas Sinton, *The Poetry of Badenoch* (1906).

One of the most obvious and tangible aspects of the Gaelic heritage of Rothiemurchus is its great legacy of Gaelic place-names and this is what this chapter will focus on. To do justice to all the Gaelic place-names found within Rothiemurchus would require an entire book, so this study will concern itself with only the names of the main topographical features found on the estate.

Gaelic Place-Names of Rothiemurchus

Area Names

Rothiemurchus
Ràt Mhurchais, 'the fort of Murchas'.
Since the Rev. Patrick Grant in the *Statistical Account* of 1791 stated that the

name signified 'the great plain of the fir', most people have accepted this meaning. The phonetics of the name, however, do not support this interpretation and it is much more likely that the name means 'the fort of Murchas' (Watson 1926: 517). The fort referred to is probably the structure which used to stand on the top of the hillock beside the Doune.

The Cairngorms

Am Monadh Ruadh, 'the russet-coloured mountain range'.

Being made of pink granite, it very often appears russet red in the light of the setting sun.

[To get best use of the following list one should consult Figure 2.1. The numbers and letters correspond with those in the panorama. Only those features found within the bounds of Rothiemurchus are given in this list. The Ordnance Survey form of the name and grid reference are given first. This is followed by the Gaelic form of the name which the local pronunciation suggests and then comments on its possible derivation.]

Hills, Mountains & Ridges

1. *Callart Hill* (918139)
   An Call-Ord, 'the hazel hill'.
   Mr Ian Fraser of the Scottish Place-names Survey tells me that place-names with the element **òrd** for 'hill' are very commonly found on borders between districts. This is the case here, for this hill lies on the border between Rothiemurchus and Pityoulish.

2. *Creag Phitiùlais* (931133)
   Am Meall Buidhe, 'the yellow hill'.

3. *Creag a' Ghreusaiche* (942124)
   Creag a' Ghreusaiche, 'the crag of the cobbler'.

4. *Cairn Lochan* (986027)
   Càrn an Lochain, 'the cairn of the lochan'.

5. *Creag an Leth-choin* (967034)
   Creag an Leth-Choin, 'the crag of the lurcher'.
   A tale used to be told in Rothiemurchus of how this mountain got its name. It told of a great deer hunt, using lurcher dogs, which began above Ryvoan and continued across the mountains until *Creag an Leth-Choin* was reached. There, an exhausted stag fell over the rocks and a lurcher dog, in its eagerness to pursue it, jumped after it to its death.

6. *Castle Hill* (958059)
   An Caisteal, 'the castle'.
   Variant **An Caisteal Sgròbach**, 'the striated castle'.

7. *Creag a' Chalmain* (962053)
   Creag a' Chalmain, 'the crag of the dove'.

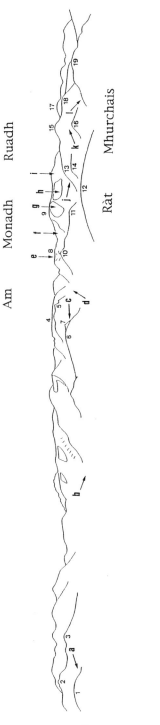

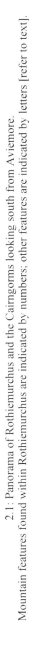

2.1: Panorama of Rothiemurchus and the Cairngorms looking south from Aviemore.
Mountain features found within Rothiemurchus are indicated by numbers; other features are indicated by letters [refer to text].

Variant **Creag nan Calman**, 'the crag of the doves'.
Although this seems an unlikely place to be frequented by doves, the ornithologist Roy Dennis tells me that this is not inconceivable and that the stock dove is found in Asia, in the presence of agricultural activity, up to altitudes of 18,000 feet. In olden times there were shielings quite close to this hill where people tended their farm animals during the summer months, so it seems possible that the stock dove may indeed have once frequented this area.

8. *Sròn na Lairige* (964012)
   Sròn na Làirige, 'the promontory of the pass'.

9. *Braeriach* (953999)
   Am Bràigh Riabhach, 'the grey-brown speckled upland'.

10. *Carn Eilrig* (938053)
    Càrn Eileirg, 'the cairn of the deertrap'.
    The place-name element **eileirg** (usual English form *elrick*) is found in many places in Scotland from Inverness-shire southwards (Watson 1926:184). It signifies a narrow, v-shaped defile into which deer were driven at one end by parties of beaters, while at the other end hunters waited in ambush.
    An account of such a hunt taking place in Mar Forest, just a few miles from here, is given by John Taylor in *The Pennylesse Pilgrimage*, a book which was written in 1618. The **eileirg** referred to in this place-name is the narrow entrance to Gleann Einich which lies below the hill.

11. *Carn a' Phris-ghiubhais* (934032)
    Càrn a' Phris Ghiuthais, 'the cairn of the clump of pine trees'.

12. *Tullochgrue* (9109)
    Tulach Dhrù, 'the hill of the (river) Druie'.

13. *Cadha Mòr* (912057)
    An Cadha Mòr, 'the big steep-faced ridge'.
    Dwelly's *Gaelic to English Dictionary* (the most authoritative of all Gaelic to English dictionaries) gives the meaning of **cadha** as being 'pass'. Although this is the meaning which I have found that this word has in the northern Hebrides, in the Cairngorm area it always seems to mean 'a steep face' or 'a steep-faced ridge'. Dwelly further says that this word is often "erroneously translated as 'brae' in Sutherland", but in the Gaelic poem entitled 'Bighouse's Farewell to the Forest' by the Sutherland poet Rob Donn it is clearly used to signify 'a steep slope', so the Cairngorm area may not be the only one in which **cadha** has this meaning.

14. *Cadha Beag* (9106)
    An Cadha Beag, 'the little steep-faced ridge'.

15. *Creag Dhubh* (906043)

A' Chreag Dhubh, 'the black crag'.

16. *Creagan Bun Suinn* (9006)
    Creagan Bun Suinn, 'the little crag at the bottom of the rampart'.
    Variant **Creagan Cinn Suinn**, 'the little crag at the end of the rampart'.
    Viewed from the east or the west this hill does indeed look like a rampart.

17. *Sgòran Dubh Mòr* (906004)
    An Sgòran Dubh, 'the black peak'.

18. *Creag Fhiaclach* (898055)
    A' Chreag Fhiaclach, 'the toothy crag'.
    There are a number of rocky bluffs on the face of this hill and it is these
    which are referred to by the adjective 'toothy'.

19. *Ord Bàn* (892086)
    An t-Ord Bàn, 'the light-coloured hill'.
    The word **òrd** used for 'hill' here is, as already noted, often found on the
    borders between districts. This hill lies very close to the border between
    Rothiemurchus and Inshriach.

Other Features

a. *Loch Pityoulish* (9213)
   Loch Peit Gheollais, 'the loch of the settlement of the bright place'.
   Peit is a word of Pictish origins which originally meant 'portion of land', but
   eventually came to signify 'settlement'. It is common in place-names
   throughout the north of Scotland. In districts where Gaelic is still spoken, this
   Pictish element in these place-names has been replaced by the Gaelic one
   baile (same meaning). This was also the case with Pityoulish, for it is
   recorded that it was at one point known as 'Ballegealish' (Lobban 1989: 71).

b. *Loch Morlich* (9609)
   Loch Mòrlaich.
   The meaning of this name is very unclear. It may be related to the second
   element in the names Ard*vorlich* and Ben *Vorlich* (found on both Loch
   Lomond and Loch Earn). It has been suggested that in these instances it
   derives from the Early Gaelic **muirbolc** and means 'bag-shaped bay'
   (Watson 1926: 80). 'Bag-shaped bay' is a fair description of the bay at the
   head of Loch Morlich. Another possibility is **Loch Mòr-Thulaich**, 'the loch
   of the big hillock'. There is a large hillock at the south west corner of the loch
   which is now known as **An Sìthean Mòr**, 'the big fairy hillock' and it is
   conceivable that it could have been called **Mòr-Thulach** in earlier times.
   Whatever the meaning, it is recorded that both *Morlich* (in this name) and the
   place-name *Mortlach* (in Banffshire) were pronounced in a similar fashion in
   Gaelic (Diack 1944: 190).

c. *Chalamain Gap* (9605)
   Eag Coire na Còmhdhalach, 'the gorge of the corrie of the meeting'.
   Variant **Eag Coire a' Choinneachaidh**, (same meaning).
   The use of the name *Chalamain Gap* for this feature is grossly incorrect.

d. *Lairig Ghru* (9602)
   Làirig Dhrù, 'the pass of the (river) Druie'.
   The Druie has its source in this pass. There is still a verb in Gaelic **drùdh**, which means 'soak' and this river name would seem to be derived from the same root.

e. *Coire Gorm* (9502)
   An Coire Gorm, 'the green corrie'.
   Although most books for learners of Gaelic say that **gorm** means 'blue', this is not the whole story - the colour system in Gaelic was originally much more complicated than that of English, being what linguists term 'attributive'. This means that the word used to describe a colour in Gaelic was dependent on which particular object was being referred to. One result of this was that the same Gaelic word could be used to describe different colours of different types of object. **Gorm** meant 'blue' when used in reference to *the sky*, but 'green' when used in reference to *grass.* **An Coire Gorm**, like other corries of the same name in the Cairngorms is a grassy corrie, so the name quite clearly means 'the green corrie'.

f. *Coire Beanaidh* (9501)
   Coire Beanaidh, 'the corrie of the (river) Bennie'.
   One of the sources of the Bennie is found in this corrie.

g. *Coire Ruadh* (9400 & 9500)
   An Coire Ruadh, 'the russet-coloured corrie'.
   This is an apt description for this corrie which is full of granite scree.

h. *Coire an Lochain* (9400)
   Coire an Lochain, 'the corrie of the lochan'.

i. (*No name given*) (9300)
   A' Bhuidheanach, 'the yellow place'.

j. *Gleann Einich* (9201)
   Gleann Eanaich, 'the glen of the bog'.
   An apt description, for much of the bottom of this glen is covered by peat bog.

k. *Coire Buidhe* (9005)
   An Coire Buidhe, 'the yellow corrie'.

l. *Loch an Eilein* (8907)
   Loch an Eilein, 'the loch of the island'.

Acknowledgements

One of the principal meanings of the word 'heritage' is anything that has been handed down from the past or handed down by tradition, so it would seem appropriate here to name those tradition-bearers who passed down to me much of the information which I possess regarding the Gaelic place-names of Rothiemurchus: Miss Mary Cameron, Tulloch; Mr John Carr, Aviemore; Mr Jim Collie, Rothiemurchus; Mr William Collie (Tullochgrue), Rothiemurchus; Mr Bob Davidson, Rothiemurchus; Mrs Mary Grant, Nethybridge; Mr Andrew Kennedy, Speybank; Mr Alex MacGregor, Drumguish; Miss Grace MacGregor, Drumguish; Mr Billy MacKenzie, Aviemore; Mr Pat MacLean, Nethybridge; Miss Jessie MacPherson, Aviemore; Mr Hamish Reid, Rothiemurchus; Mr Donald Smith, Lurg; Mr Noel Smith, Nethybridge; Mr Brock Nethersole-Thomson, Rothiemurchus; Mrs Carrie Nethersole-Thomson, Rothiemurchus and all members of the maternal side of my own family (the Mackintosh family of 'Woodlands', Rothiemurchus).

I wish also to acknowledge the debt which this study owes to the work of Professor William J. Watson (1865–1948), the foremost pioneer in Scottish place-name research.

Bibliography

Diack, Francis C. 1944: *The Inscriptions of Pictland.* Aberdeen.

Dwelly, Edward 1920: *The Illustrated Gaelic-English Dictionary.* Glasgow.

Grannd, Seumas 1986: *Oran Bron er Dearn Graunt le Shemis G. Diarn Rathamurch* (Published in *Scottish Gaelic Studies*, Vol 14).

Lobban, Gillies 1989: *Gillies Lobban's Manuscript* (Published posthumously in *The Transactions of the Gaelic Society of Inverness*, Vol 55).

Morrison, Hew 1899: *Songs and Poems in the Gaelic Language by Rob Donn.* Edinburgh.

Sinton, Thomas 1906: *The Poetry of Badenoch.* Inverness.

Taylor, John 1618: *The Pennylesse Pilgrimage.* London.

Watson, William J. 1926: *History of the Celtic Place-Names of Scotland.* Edinburgh.

3. The Grant Lairds of Rothiemurchus

Chris Smout

This short chapter on the Grant lairds is not intended to be exhaustive, but it is necessary to set the background to much else that follows in this book, particularly with respect to Elizabeth Grant's father and brothers, whose tenure of the estate between them covered the entire nineteenth century.

The Grants have been in possession of Rothiemurchus for a very long time. The first to style himself Grant of Rothiemurchus was James, Chief of Grant and third laird of Freuchie, who died in 1553. He attempted to exchange land in Nairn and Angus for Rothiemurchus, by a transaction with the Dallases of Cantray, but it all fell through. His son got a better title by purchase from the Earl of Huntly but effective possession (and the final expulsion of the Shaw lairds who had possessed the estate in late medieval times) should perhaps be dated to 1580, when a younger grandson of that James, Patrick Grant of Muckerach, took over the estate. Even then his father, who died in 1585, stated in his will that Patrick was 'inquietit' in the estate that he had provided for him, and left him corn, cattle, sheep, gold and silver, 'to support him in his trouble'. From that point on the Grants of Rothiemurchus became distinct from the senior branch, the Grants of Grant, whose power became consolidated down the Spey, at Abernethy and Grantown[1] (for a family tree, see Appendix 2).

So for more than four centuries the Grants of Rothiemurchus have been owners and stewards of this remarkable estate. It is very unusual, particularly for a family that is not of the peerage, to own an estate so long in unbroken succession; indeed, the record could be exceeded only by a few of the nobility, such as the Dukes of Argyll in the west and the Dukes of Buccleuch in the south.

Such continuity was a function both of luck and skill. It was luck that provided the Grants with a plentiful supply of male heirs, so that, of the thirteen transfers of heirs since 1580, eleven have been to sons, one to a nephew (Elizabeth Grant's father) and one to a younger brother (Elizabeth Grant's brother). Consequently the estate never became swallowed up in the dowry of a daughter and so lost to the Grant name. The survival of an estate in the seventeenth and eighteenth centuries, however, was also a matter of avoiding political catastrophe, and here the family blended luck with judgement. The Grants of Rothiemurchus, as cadets of the powerful Grants of Grant, followed the political lead of their chiefs, which brought them to oppose James VII's cause in 1690 and to back the Hanoverians in the eighteenth century. Safety, however, was sometimes a close run thing. Patrick, the sixth laird, was a friend of Rob Roy Macgregor, whose Jacobite and unconventional activities would not have made him a comfortable ally. James, the seventh laird, found himself in command of a small Grant garrison at Inverness Castle (Fort George, as it was then called) when it surrendered to the Jacobite forces in 1745: he and other leading Grant gentlemen were then held hostage by the rebels as security for the good behaviour of their clan, on whose behalf they readily promised neutrality. All this took some explaining in a letter to the Duke of Cumberland upon their release after Culloden: he was court-martialled but avoided serious retribution. Nevertheless the ease with which Colonel Roy Stewart, the fugitive Jacobite poet, found shelter on the Rothiemurchus estate in the following months, at least suggests a continued ambiguity on the part of the laird (perhaps because James Grant was a Gaelic poet himself: see Appendix 1, p 143). Furthermore, his wife Jean Gordon, *alias* Grizel Mhor, was a well-known Jacobite lady who according to tradition, sheltered fugitives near Loch-an-Eilein.[2]

So the Grants hung on to Rothiemurchus in these troubled times, in contrast, for example, to their neighbours over the hill, the Earls of Mar, who lost their lands after the 1715, or the owners of the biggest Caledonian pine woods in the west, Cameron of Lochiel, whose house was burned and estate forfeited in 1746. They consolidated their reputation for loyalty in the generations that followed by almost unbroken military or civil service stretching over two centuries.

In the story of survival it was also important that in 1787 Patrick, the eighth laird, when his nephew and heir John Peter was only thirteen, enacted a deed of entail over Rothiemurchus. This legal device, widely used in the eighteenth and nineteenth centuries, made it legally impossible to sell the estate. Through entail, heirs effectively became life tenants of their own lands. An entail generally made it more difficult to raise loans for capital improvements, since the creditors could not seize and sell the estate if the borrowers defaulted. On the other hand, while it could not pass from the ownership of the family, if the incumbent did default the creditors could form a trust to administer it until their losses were recouped from rentals and similar income.

Patrick, who in other ways showed himself a shrewd and cautious man, may have had an inkling of his heir's extravagant proclivities even at that tender age. Elizabeth Grant, with devastating and unsentimental candour, has portrayed her father's feckless character only too clearly. He was ultimately to mire the estate in problems from which it perhaps did not fully recover for the better part of 150 years.

John Peter inherited the estate in 1790 and married six years later. He was already heir to '£10,000 in ready money' from his father William Grant, who had very successfully practised medicine in London. He soon found that he had acquired another fortune when his wife inherited from her elder sister, the widow of a rich Glasgow merchant and, to cap it all, another uncle left him an estate in Hertfordshire worth £1,200 a year in addition to the rental of £800 a year from Rothiemurchus itself. As the Highland Lady put it: 'Life began with these happy young people well. To assist in the spending of what was then a fine income, there were numberless relations on both sides...' Soon even his inheritance did not seem enough. In 1808 he was able, by obtaining a private Act of Parliament, to have the conditions of the entail on Rothiemurchus varied so as to allow him, effectively, unfettered access to the money raised by selling timber. This in 1811 enabled him to borrow substantial sums from his cousin, James Grant of Burnhall, WS and banker, and others, using the wood as security.[3] The remainder of the estate stayed entailed.

John Peter had been trained as a lawyer, and had ambitions to succeed at the bar first in Edinburgh and then in London. In both he failed, but his final undoing was to switch his attention to politics, entering the House of Commons as MP first for Great Grimsby and then for Tavistock, which occupied the years from 1812 to 1827. The sums needed to bribe and nurse an electorate in the unreformed Parliament proved, in conjunction with the unabated extravagance of his life style, to be beyond his means. By 1824 he was in effect bankrupt, with debts amounting to £65,000. A trust was already in being to receive money from the woods to repay his obligations. It was now restructured, empowered to take over all his other moveable assets. In 1827 he simultaneously lost his seat in Parliament and the ability to fend off his creditors – 'without this shield his person was not safe'. They could not seize and sell the lands of Rothiemurchus because of the entail, but they took what they could of the family's personal possessions, and John Peter, his wife and children fled to India, literally fending off the tradesmen as they went.[4]

The woods and estate of Rothiemurchus thus came from 1827 to be administered by trustees acting on behalf of the creditors, and the Doune was rented in 1830 to the Duchess of Bedford as a retreat for herself and her lover, the portrait painter Edwin Landseer. John Peter at the age of 53 embarked on a new and more successful legal career in the Empire, ultimately becoming Chief Justice of Calcutta. He died at sea in 1848 at the age of 74, attempting to return home to Britain.[5]

The Grants reassumed actual control of the estate from the trustees around 1842 following a complex arrangement whereby the original trust was bought out for £14,700 by a new one headed by his daughter Jane's father-in-law, William Gibson Craig, and the debt on the estate was largely, though not entirely, paid off by 1845, probably mainly by felling the woods. In April 1845 Elizabeth reported that by the end of the year her father and eldest brother, William Patrick, would have:

> ... paid off the debt as compromised with the creditors at large, William £30,000, my father rather more than £20,000. But there is a class of private friends whom they propose to pay in full which will take £8000 more — Uncle Ralph, Mrs. Cooper etc., very right, but why not me, the smallness of the sum don't make any difference surely... it's out of sight out of mind with my father.

All she wanted, as she explained, was 'a good grand pianoforte as my kind aunt meant I should always have', and which had been one of the household goods seized by the creditors.[6]

So the debts amounted, even when creditors had been paid something considerably less than twenty shillings to the pound, to a sum well in excess of £60,000. It is worth recalling that the average value of an unmarried Scottish farm servant's annual wage in 1843, including benefits in kind, was around £20, that the parish schoolmaster's annual salary in Duthil in 1853 was under £26 (though the minister's stipend was £242) and that John Peter's own widow was expected by her son in 1849 to live on between £400 and £500 a year – 'she has ample for her own wants', said Elizabeth.[7] Several of the creditors were impoverished or ruined, most notably James Grant of Burnhall W.S., who had provided the original loan on the woods in 1811, and was himself bankrupt and in the hands of creditors in 1829.[8] Elizabeth Grant's verdict on the whole sorrowful story came when she was contemplating her father's portrait in the Doune, 'pale and sad', on her return visit in 1846:

> To have been born Laird of Rothiemurchus should have satisfied the most ambitious spirit. To have thrown such an inheritance away would, if reflected on, have brought *brown* hairs down with sorrow to the grave.[9]

The following two lairds, brothers of the Highland Lady, spent, like their father, much time in imperial service, having emigrated with the rest of the family in 1827. William Patrick's career as a barrister and judge in India was at first successful, but plunged into disaster in 1848 when he was closely involved as one of two active directors in the massive collapse of the Union Bank of Calcutta – 'it began with a capital of a million, seven eighths of which have disappeared', reported Elizabeth, adding, 'William is not a man I should like to have any dealings with – speculating, arrogant, and I am afraid selfish'. He was cleared of criminal wrongdoing, but lost his house and furniture in Calcutta and a coffee plantation in Ceylon, 'and of course the rents of Rothiemurchus whenever the claims already on it are paid up'. The extent of his Indian debt was a staggering £72,000. He was therefore already penniless when he returned to become the tenth laird of Rothiemurchus later the same year.[10]

In a slightly more charitable mood his sister lamented that her 'dear, absurd brother's judgement' was not equal to his intellect:

> But he is not all to blame. His education was thoroughly vicious. A spoiled childhood, a publick school, the low dissipation of college, a habit of debt, a scramble for money all round him, a very unhappy home, and the means not forthcoming to give him his profession.[11]

It is not clear what the financial situation of Rothiemurchus was during the following quarter century of William Patrick's lairdship, but the estate was certainly sequestered around 1855 and administered again for some years by trustees acting for creditors, though the laird seems to have been back in the saddle by 1861. By a strange arrangement, the life interest in the estate of

William Patrick was put up to public roup in Edinburgh in 1855 and bought for £2,000 by his sister Jane. This must have been a device for keeping management in the family while satisfying the law. Certainly William Patrick was easily the busiest and most effective of all the nineteenth-century land managers of the estate: even in the 1820s he was more interested in management than his father. His own regime really began, however, in 1842, when he began to manage Rothiemurchus at a distance by extraordinarily detailed correspondence from Calcutta, and lasted, albeit with interruption, until his death in 1874.[12]

In 1868 he wrote to his brother and heir a long letter, listing all that he had done for the estate. He claimed to have laid out £30,000 in improvements over the years, and listed five achievements of his management. Firstly, he had increased the yearly rental of the estate from less than £1,000 per annum to over £2,300, 'at which sum I was assessed for income tax, on account of it, last year'. Secondly, he had built a bridge across the Spey, constructed many miles of road, spanned a ford and opened 'easy communication between all parts of the estate and the railway station at Aviemore'. Thirdly, he had 'made a great length of permanent fence, by which all cattle and sheep on the estate are confined within bounds and prevented from destroying the trees which are springing up naturally all over the ground'. Fourthly, he had protected the low ground from Spey floods by building about five miles of embankment. Lastly, he had improved the amenity of the Doune by carrying out repairs and 'extending the house grounds to the limits pointed out by nature'.[13]

It remains a mystery how, given his past reputation, he raised the necessary capital for all this work, but beyond question he transformed the estate. Much of the superstructure of estate communication, building and protection on which management depends today is the far-sighted work of William Patrick.

His successor was his and Elizabeth's younger brother, the second John Peter. His character was very different from that of William Patrick, a fact which also comes across very clearly in Elizabeth's journals. He was an imperial servant of the highest probity and skill, entering the service of the East India Company in 1828, serving on the commission for the suppression of human sacrifice in Garjam in 1844 (this referred to the Hindu practice of 'suttee', by which a widow was expected to throw herself onto her husband's funeral pyre), promoted to be Lieutenant Governor of the Central Provinces in 1857-9, playing a distinguished role during the mutiny, acting as Lieutenant Governor of Bengal, 1859-62 and then transferring to the other side of the world to be Captain General of Jamaica and becoming responsible for creating its code of civil laws, 1866-73.[14]

He was awarded a knighthood KCB, GCMG, for all these good works, and returned to Rothiemurchus in his mid-sixties. Immediately he set about spending £4,520 on reconstructing the Doune with Lascelles as architect, but shortly thereafter discovered that his colonial pension and the modest rents of Rothiemurchus did not allow him to live in it, and the Doune became, for the first time, a hotel.[15] Nevertheless, he still hankered after making improvements on the estate which almost led Rothiemurchus once more to financial catastrophe.

In June 1887, his eldest son wrote to a relative to tell him that 'there has taken place in the affairs of our revered parents a financial crisis'. A creditor named Brodie had demanded repayment of £4,300 advanced for improvements on the estate: the laird had been unable to meet the demand, and Brodie tried to insist, first, that Sir John Peter and Lady Grant live all year on their estates, secondly that he surrendered all his income to Brodie, including his pension, and thirdly that Lady Grant submitted their household accounts to Brodie for auditing. 'It did my father a lot of good for he cussed and foamed at the mouth for a whole day and had a splendid appetite in consequence.' The old man (he was in his eightieth year) was apparently unaware that he had £10,000 in stocks which he could use partly to pay off Brodie. His son arranged the necessary sale, fired some 'lazy servants' and tried to make his father understand that he could not just 'order houses and bridges to be built whenever he takes the fancy into his head'.[16]

At this period, the estate's value as a sporting let became of increasing importance, leading to conflicts over rights of way and access that were not finally resolved until well into the twentieth century.

The five lairds who have followed in succession after the death of Sir John Peter in 1893 were all also named John Peter. It is a kindness to future historians that the son of the present Mr and Mrs John Peter Grant has been named James. It is not the intention to follow their careers in the same detail as the Highland Lady's immediate relatives. It is sufficient to say that they have been distinguished in the service of their country in various ways, both civil and military, and the last four have been generally resident at Rothiemurchus except when military service demanded otherwise. Memories of the present laird's grandfather and father, respectively 'the Sheriff' and 'the Colonel', are still very much alive, and affectionately held, in Strathspey.

By degrees, and with difficulty, the family recovered in financial terms from the legacy of the Highland Lady's relations, despite the weakening of the legal protection afforded by entail in this century and, especially in the 1920s, some very difficult times for landed estates everywhere.

Not least remarkable has been the achievement of recent decades in which the estate has improved turnover and multiplied jobs by embracing, rather than resisting, the wish of an urban population to enjoy to the full the very best of the countryside. Since Rothiemurchus has retained such exceptional qualities of beauty and interest, it is no wonder it now has a worldwide band of admirers.

The essential question to an environmental historian is whether it matters, from the point of view of its survival as a place of such natural heritage importance, that Rothiemurchus has been in the hands of one family for four-and-a-half centuries. Is this a relevant factor in its present environmental character and landscape appearance? The lairds, after all, were very different individuals, some good land managers, some not, some capable with money, others absolutely the reverse. Taking the entire period, they were much more often at home on their estates than absent, though for parts of the nineteenth century they certainly were absentee over long periods. Present or not, their management often led to drastic action that the twentieth century would baulk at, such as clear-felling most of the Caledonian pine in an attempt to liquidate their debts.

Yet the continuity of the family on the estate does clearly matter, for two reasons. Firstly, the Grants have taken the long term view, certainly from the moment in 1787 when the eighth laird, Patrick, entailed the land. Even William Patrick, in India the ultimate speculator ('how could an honest mind stoop to the chicanery of gambling traders' arts' asked his sister), spent £30,000 on the superstructure of an estate from which he could not possibly have expected to see a return in his lifetime. The strong sense of being stewards of the land, guarding for posterity rather than raiding for the here-and-now, has certainly imbued recent generations of Grant lairds. They do not give the appearance of being here to mine the land, or to use it as a toy for a decade or two, but rather to hand it on, in as good or better condition as they found it, to their successors. Since Rothiemurchus has now become recognised as a place of national significance for its natural and scenic qualities, that also means a commitment to hand it on to our successors as well.

The second point is that the Grant lairds really appear to have loved the estate. To Elizabeth it was 'our beloved Duchus'. Her father, having in effect been driven from it by his own folly and profligacy, died on board ship at the age of 74 attempting to return to it. Her elder brother's letters in the 1840s, managing Rothiemurchus from Calcutta, were informed by a minute knowledge and affection for every inch of it, and when his debts again drove him from it in the 1850s, his factor wrote to assure him that 'Rothiemurchus is more beautiful than ever, and in the summer a perfect nonesuch'.[17] Her younger brother's love of its natural heritage earned him, posthumously, a medal from the Zoological Society for his pioneering efforts to protect its ospreys.[18] When the fourteenth laird, John Peter 'the Sheriff', was faced in the Second World War with the requisitioning of his pine forests, he bargained with the authorities that the Canadian lumberjacks should start at the edge of the estate and cut the trees round Loch an Eilein only as a last resort; hostilities ended before they plucked the jewel from the crown. Both he and his successor 'the Colonel' refused the blandishments to sell to the Forestry Commission, and so to turn Rothiemurchus into a second Glenmore of alien spruce. Anyone who doubts the difference that Grant ownership of Rothiemurchus has made need only to compare that estate with the sad condition of its neighbours: Glenmore, now being determinedly rehabilitated from inappropriate plantation forestry; Mar Lodge, at a still earlier state of rehabilitation from extreme overgrazing by deer and sheep; and Glenfeshie, where little rehabilitation either from forestry or from extreme overgrazing is yet visible. Rothiemurchus starts from another plane altogether.

Such is the background of ownership of the Rothiemurchus estate against which to consider the remainder of these chapters.

Notes

1   *Burke's Landed Gentry* (edn. London, 1937), pp. 956-7; W. Fraser, *Chiefs of Grant* (Edinburgh, 1883), Vol. I, pp. 509-10; C. Innes (ed.), *Registrum Episcopatus Moraviensis* (Bannatyne Club, Edinburgh, 1837).

2   *Burke's Landed Gentry*; Fraser, *Chiefs of* Grant; D. Warrand (ed.), *More Culloden Papers* (Inverness, 1930), Vol. X, pp. 61, 74-6.

3   Elizabeth Grant, *Memoirs of a Highland Lady* (ed. A. Tod, Edinburgh, 1988), p. 7; Doune papers, unnumbered bundle called 'Titles in name of trustees for the creditors of Sir John Peter Grant; SRO: Court of Session unextracted processes, CS 96/2617, sederunt book relating to the sequestration of James Grant.

4   *Highland Lady*, pp. 199-205; Doune papers, 'titles for the creditors'.

5   Elizabeth Grant, *The Highland Lady in Ireland* (ed. P. Pelly and A. Tod, Edinburgh, 1991), pp. 244, 249-51, 406-7.

6   Elizabeth Grant, *A Highland Lady in France* (ed. P. Pelly and A.. Tod, East Linton, 1996), p. 227.

7   I. Levitt and C. Smout, *The State of the Scottish Working Class in 1843* (Edinburgh, 1979), p. 85; J.H. Dawson, *An Abridged Statistical Account of Scotland* (Edinburgh, 1853), p. 379; *Highland Lady in Ireland*, p. 487.

8   SRO: CS 96/2617.

9   *Highland Lady in Ireland*, pp. 240-1.

10 *Ibid.*, esp. pp. 372-6, 417.

11 *Ibid.*, p. 412.

12 Doune papers, 'titles for the creditors'.

13 Doune papers, 211.

14 *Burke's Landed Gentry*.

15 Doune papers, 211, 483.

16 Doune papers, 483.

17 Doune papers, 224, 225, 319.

18 See chapters 4 & 5 below.

Acknowledgement

I am grateful to John and Philippa Grant for reading through the draft chapter and drawing my attention to supplementary material, and for generous access to the archives of the Doune.

4. The Birds and Mammals of Rothiemurchus

Roy Dennis

About twenty-five years ago, Col. Iain Grant of Rothiemurchus telephoned me and said that the estate were building a new cottage near the Doune. He wanted me to check the old trees for nesting buzzards and woodpeckers' holes before they started felling. We met next morning and as we walked over the wooded hillock, which is to the east of the old house, he suddenly said: "Of course, my ancestors used to live here on this hillock." I asked "When was that, Colonel?" "It's a long time ago, maybe a thousand years, I suppose," was his reply.

He clearly was a member of the native local fauna, as is his son today. I think it is important to remind ourselves of how long people and nature have co-existed in places such as Rothiemurchus and how close the indigenous people still feel to the land.

Rothiemurchus has always been renowned for its wildlife. It was a mecca for the Victorian naturalists on the quest for rare wildlife. It has the dramatic history of the decline of the breeding ospreys at the famous castle at Loch an Eilein. The annual account of successes and tragedies during the latter part of the nineteenth century is both exciting and sad; in April 1893 the Zoological Society of London awarded a silver medal to John Peter Grant of Rothiemurchus for his attempts to safeguard the birds. Sadly, they were lost by 1900, although nowadays Rothiemurchus is once more important for ospreys.

The ancient Caledonian forest of Rothiemurchus is one of the best remaining parts of the ancient boreal forest of northern Scotland. It is very important for natural history and always has been. It is made even more special because of the rich variety of lochs and rivers, moorland and mountain, which create great diversity within the estate. It is no wonder part of it was chosen as one of Scotland's first National Nature Reserves.

It has some very special birds, like crested tits, Scottish crossbill and capercaillie. At least 173 species of birds have been recorded at Rothiemurchus, out of the 237 that have been recorded in the whole of Badenoch and Strathspey.

Of those, 101 are regular breeders. There are very few places in Britain where you can find a hundred species nesting on one estate. Another nineteen species have either been sporadic breeders or are now extinct as breeding species: for example, the corncrake, which last nested at Tullochgrue in the early 1960s but no longer does so. There are a further 53 species which are migrants or vagrants.

In total 27 species of mammals occur on Rothiemurchus and another nine are now extinct. The ancient Scots pine forests are ideal habitat for red squirrels, and the land is also excellent for red deer, roe deer, fox and badger.

A special attraction to naturalists is the fact that such different habitats are so close together. From the summits of the mountains, at Sgoran Dubh Mhor, down to the Doune is only a distance of about five miles but it is also a drop of nearly three thousand feet in altitude. This gives a great variety of wildlife in a surprisingly small area. Take, for example, just two families of birds, the grouse family and the buntings. On the high tops you find ptarmigan, and then as you walk down through the heather moorland there are red grouse; at the edge of the birchwoods there are black grouse; once in the ancient Scots pine forest one can find capercaillie and as you walk out on to the farm fields you see grey partridge and pheasant. There are very few places in Britain, or the world, where you can experience that variety of grouse.

At Rothiemurchus you can, with skill, see all of these species in a day's walk. Equally, you can listen to yellowhammers and reed buntings singing in the morning and a few hours later find breeding snow buntings at the other end of the estate. It is special to have them so relatively close together.

What was Rothiemurchus like 200 years ago, or even 2,000 years ago? How fascinating it would have been to have experienced it. People have lived in Strathspey for about 5,000 years and have had quite dramatic effects on the wild fauna. Rothiemurchus is part of the ancient boreal forest of northern Europe, the western extremity of it, and tree cover was far greater in the past. The area of present day ancient forest of Rothiemurchus, when added to the other remnant pinewoods of the Highlands is actually less than one percent of the area of the original Ancient Wood of Caledon.

As well as the loss of forest cover, we have also lost the larger mammals and some birds have become extinct. The common (or Eurasian) crane disappeared as a breeding species in the twelfth or thirteenth century, probably because it provided sport for the nobles and was good to eat. It is likely that it occurred at Rothiemurchus.

What of Rothiemurchus today? It is clearly different to its original forested state, but it is still a very special wildlife area in our country. Phil Ratcliffe, in his chapter, will detail the national and international significance of the habitats and ecology of Rothiemurchus. I will point out some of the many changes to the bird and mammal fauna over time. There have been great variations, some to do with climate changes and natural fluctuations and others relating to the impact of man, either direct persecution of the species or indirectly by changing the habitats.

We still value Rothiemurchus as an important place for birds which are rare in Britain, such as capercaillie, osprey, crested tit and Scottish crossbill, but it is also important to remember that changes have occurred over time which have dramatically changed the biodiversity of a place like Rothiemurchus.

Just over a century ago, one of the most endangered species in Scotland was the great spotted woodpecker. It was possible the bird was extinct throughout the country, but it is likely that a few pairs still nested in the old pines of Abernethy Forest. It would have been common before 1830 in Rothiemurchus and then it disappeared. Now it is present throughout mainland Scotland and is a regular nesting bird in Rothiemurchus. More recently, the green woodpecker reached Strathspey from the south, with the first records being at Kinrara and the Doune from February to March 1971. The first successful breeding was noted in 1978; now the small population has crashed and all but disappeared.

One of the most dramatic losses was the capercaillie. They had become extinct in Strathspey and Badenoch, and presumably in Rothiemurchus, before the 1770s. The last ones in Inverness-shire were seen in 1770 and the last two recorded individuals of the original Scottish stock were killed at Ballochbuie in Deeside in 1785. They must have been a historic meal!

Capercaillies were reintroduced to Scotland from Sweden from 1837 onwards; in 1875, some were released at Invereshie, not far from Rothiemurchus. The first four reached Rothiemurchus in 1890 and there then followed a slow recolonisation by the species. The maximum populations were probably reached around the 1950s and 1960s, then in the late 1970s, the species started to decline and is now in a critical state in Scotland with less than 2,000 birds. A Capercaillie Action Plan has been launched to stem the decline and aid recovery.

It is difficult for people, now, to believe that numbers were once so plentiful that the local crofters and farmers were absolutely fed up with capercaillies, black grouse and red grouse at harvest time, because the stooks of oats became so covered in their droppings that it was a very dirty task to gather in the harvest. What a difference now – for it is a bird we are all trying to protect.

Thousands and thousands of cattle were grazed in the glens, hills and forests of Strathspey in the eighteenth century. They were even taken up into the high corries in the summer. Later, came the great flocks of sheep. They had a dramatic influence on the landscape and wildlife. Of course, in some ways the cattle were replicating the effects of the ancient cattle, or aurochs, which were present when humans first arrived. Generally speaking, we say that cattle are good for wildlife, and sheep are bad. That is probably an over simplification, but it does mean that some birds benefit from cattle, and some even from intensive sheep grazing, although the latter is not ecologically sustainable.

Birds like golden plover, curlew and lapwing benefited from forest clearance and the grazing of cattle in the hills. In fact, birds of open land increased in numbers and range at the same time as truly forest species, like capercaillie and great spotted woodpeckers declined. Starlings would have increased, for in the countryside they were closely associated with cattle. A favourite food supply for them is the insect populations of cow pats. Even now, it is very much a bird that is associated with those farms that still have cattle.

The low intensive farming system which started centuries ago and was little changed until the mid 1960s in Strathspey gave ideal habitats for about twenty-five species of birds which were not associated with the original forest environment. Some of these species, like grey partridge, yellowhammer and linnet, are now in decline because of the downturn in old style agriculture.

Originally a coastal breeding species, oystercatchers arrived in Strathspey in the nineteenth century and are now widespread inland. They breed on Rothiemurchus. The black-headed gull was also very much involved with low intensity agriculture, especially the spring ploughing which provided an excellent food supply at egg-laying time. Nowadays, spring ploughing on hill farms and crofts is much reduced and as elsewhere in the Highlands, the black-headed gull on Rothiemurchus is much scarcer than it was earlier in the century.

Table 1: List of birds recorded on Rothiemurchus
(for status, see *Birds of Badenoch & Strathspey* 1995)

Red-throated diver, black-throated diver, great northern diver, little grebe, slavonian grebe, fulmar, cormorant, grey heron, mute swan, whooper swan, bean goose, pink-footed goose, white-fronted goose, greylag goose, Canada goose, wigeon, gadwall, teal, mallard, pintail, pochard, ring-necked duck, tufted duck, scaup, long-tailed duck, goldeneye, red-breasted merganser, goosander, honey buzzard, red kite, white-tailed eagle, marsh harrier, hen harrier, goshawk, sparrowhawk, buzzard, rough-legged buzzard, golden eagle, osprey, kestrel, merlin, hobby, peregrine, red grouse, ptarmigan, black grouse, capercaillie, red-legged partridge, grey partridge, quail, pheasant, water rail, corncrake, moorhen, coot, oystercatcher, ringed plover, dotterel, golden plover, lapwing, knot, sanderling, Temminck's stint, dunlin, snipe, woodcock, bar-tailed godwit, whimbrel, curlew, spotted redshank, redshank, greenshank, green sandpiper, wood sandpiper, common sandpiper, red-necked phalarope, arctic skua, black-headed gull, common gull, lesser black-backed gull, herring gull, great black-backed gull, kittiwake, common tern, black tern, stock dove, woodpigeon, collared dove, turtle dove, cuckoo, barn owl, snowy owl, tawny owl, long-eared owl, short-eared owl, nightjar, swift, kingfisher, hoopoe, wryneck, green woodpecker, great spotted woodpecker, skylark, shorelark, sand martin, swallow, house martin, tree pipit, meadow pipit, yellow wagtail, grey wagtail, pied wagtail, waxwing, dipper, wren, dunnock, robin, redstart, whinchat, stonechat, wheatear, ring ouzel, blackbird, fieldfare, song thrush, redwing, mistle thrush, grasshopper warbler, sedge warbler, lesser whitethroat, whitethroat, garden warbler, blackcap, wood warbler, chiffchaff, willow warbler, goldcrest, spotted flycatcher, pied flycatcher, long-tailed tit, willow tit, crested tit, coal tit, blue tit, great tit, treecreeper, red-backed shrike, great grey shrike, magpie, jackdaw, rook, carrion crow, raven, starling, house sparrow, chaffinch, brambling, greenfinch, goldfinch, siskin, linnet, twite, redpoll, common crossbill, Scottish crossbill, common rosefinch, bullfinch, hawfinch, Lapland bunting, snow bunting, yellowhammer, reed bunting, corn bunting.

The house sparrow arrived in the 1880s and has recently disappeared from many hill farms and crofts. The skylark is another bird that originally increased in line with the farming activity of our forefathers and is now in decline. Even in areas where pesticides have never been used, the skylark has gone. About ten years ago we lost the skylarks from our croft, which is about ten miles from Rothiemurchus. Grey partridge, which noticeably increased in the early years of the nineteenth century, is another bird which has seriously declined in Strathspey.

Quite dramatic changes have taken place in the bird life of the farmed land. It is as though the few outlying crofts and hill farms, places like Tullochgrue on Rothiemurchus, are no longer viable habitats for species associated with mixed low intensive agriculture. An extreme example is the corn bunting, which used to be in Strathspey in the heyday of oat growing but was lost fifty or sixty years ago. Now it has all but disappeared from the whole of the Highlands because of changes in agriculture.

I sometimes wonder if these changes are important. Some open-land species have huge ranges elsewhere in Europe and Asia. Some birds have their population highs because of our activities, and we need to be very careful about safeguarding those that may have been the result of land practices which we would no longer see as ecologically sound.

Some birds benefited, and those that could live in heather did the best of the lot. Two birds in particular colonised vast areas as they changed from forest to heather moorlands. One was the meadow pipit, which is a far more common bird now than it was, say, five hundred years ago. The other is the red grouse. Grouse reached their zenith in numbers at the turn of the century and ever since have been slipping away.

I remember when I first went to Rothiemurchus in 1960 as a nineteen year old, Colonel Grant told me about many interesting birds in the area. One which remains in my memory is the greenshank. A large area of the forest near Loch Morlich was clear-felled during the Second World War. In 1960, it was a burnt, open moor and it seemed to me to be covered in greenshanks. I think there were six pairs of greenshanks, and previously there were more, in fact a large enough population for Desmond Nethersole-Thompson to study and then to write his famous monograph on the species. There is not a single one there now for the trees have returned. I cannot bemoan that fact, for it is clear that the forest should be there. The greenshanks were transients taking advantage of our destruction of the natural habitat.

The Victorian era and the fashion for sporting estates, gave rise to an incredible onslaught on all predators, with large numbers of birds of prey being killed. I do not believe that Rothiemurchus was in that league, because very early on the Grants showed clear commitment to protecting ospreys and golden eagles, but even an estate as large as Rothiemurchus cannot sustain populations of predatory birds when land use and attitudes change over the whole country.

At that time, Rothiemurchus lost its breeding red kites. It was one of the last places where the red kite nested in Scotland, with a pair nesting there in 1878, but they had gone by 1892. The recent reintroduction of the species from

Sweden may allow them to return to their ancestral haunts in Rothiemurchus. The goshawk was specially protected in Rothiemurchus Forest in early times for the use of the bishops of Moray; some of the last pairs in Scotland lingered in these forests until the 1870s; soon after they became extinct.

The buzzard was extinct from Rothiemurchus for probably fifty years or more, and it was not until after the last war that the buzzard made its first tentative steps back into Strathspey. It is now a common bird, and rightly so. There have always been golden eagles on Rothiemurchus, and it would have been one estate where golden eagles were protected. The golden eagle situation in Scotland in the last century was complex. On most sporting estates they were hated by game preservers and destroyed, but in some places where they stalked deer, they protected golden eagles – the reason given being that the eagles killed grouse, and the noisy grouse were considered a nuisance when on a stalk, for they gave away the stalker's presence to the stags.

I actually think that some landowners just liked golden eagles because they were involved in their history, in their relationship with the land, going right back into time. It is a great pleasure that the eagles are still here. Their nesting eyries are historic places, the same places being used for centuries. The nesting sites on Rothiemurchus which I first studied in the 1960s were the very same that Seton Gordon visited in the early years of the century.

Since 1800, there have been dramatic changes in wildfowl. There are some very beautiful lochans on Rothiemurchus which are ideal nesting habitat for a variety of ducks. Some of the species that we regard as common birds now were not present as breeding birds at the time that we are celebrating. The goosander arrived in Strathspey in 1892; the wigeon in the 1890s, and the red-breasted merganser and the tufted duck in 1900. Whether this was a new colonisation or was a re-colonisation of lost range is not known. In some ways, I tend towards a recovery of range following overuse of the original stock for food in earlier centuries.

The jackdaw was a new bird for Rothiemurchus as well, as it spread up through Britain. I was reading some notes about Loch an Eilein castle and the ospreys, and several people bemoaned the fact that the jackdaws started to breed in the castle at the end of the last century and wondered if they would interfere with the osprey.

The carrion crow is a much more recent arrival in Rothiemurchus and the north of Scotland, slowly replacing the original hooded crow in the latter half of this century. The first collared dove for Inverness-shire was recorded at the Dell Hotel in Rothiemurchus on 2 July 1961, and from there they spread to colonise and live in most of our villages.

Up on the mountains the bird life has not varied so much due to human activities, but varies in line with climatic changes. Ptarmigan have been present since not long after the last Ice Age and they still live on the mountains of Rothiemurchus. The numbers of dotterel have varied quite considerably: they reached their lowest point in historical knowledge in the 1950s and 1960s. With the advent of colder springs in the 1970s and early 1980s, the dotterel population is now much higher than it was fifty years ago. We do not know how that compares with two hundred years ago, although the species was recorded as declining in the 1860s.

The same is true for the snow bunting, which is a very rare breeding species in Britain. In the early part of this century, only an occasional pair of snow buntings nested in Scotland. Nowadays, there could be a hundred pairs in the Scottish mountains in the best years and there will be half a dozen or more pairs on the high tops of Rothiemurchus. Early this century, snow buntings arriving in autumn from the Arctic were highly prized for food by the local people.

Loch an Eilein has always been famous for ospreys, principally because of the sad history of the birds trying to nest on the castle. From 1846, we have the results for twenty-four of those years: thirteen times they had their eggs robbed; twice they were disturbed; once they were shot, and they had young in eight years, so it was a difficult time for ospreys. They were quite likely to end up as a taxidermy specimen or their eggs adorning an egg collection. If you want to read some quite stirring stuff of yesteryear, read the exploits of the people who used to go to Loch an Eilein to raid the nests (see chapter 5).

It was not surprising that the Grants had a difficult time in protecting ospreys, and in 1893 John Peter Grant of Rothiemurchus was given the Zoological Society of London's silver medal for protecting these birds and attempting to secure the population. They last nested there in 1899 and for a few years after that they came and visited.

Nowadays Rothiemurchus is well known for ospreys again and in fact the late Colonel Grant received the RSPB medal in 1960. One of the best places to see them fishing is at the fish farm at Inverdruie, where you can see them well. Recently, we have been allowed to do some interesting research, using radio transmitters, on the hierarchies of breeding male ospreys and how they compete to catch fish alongside their neighbours. Ospreys breed in a loose colonial way and we have learnt that space for fishing is likely to be a controlling factor on the population. In Strathspey, ospreys have already reached that ceiling.

Another rare bird which is special to Rothiemurchus is the goldeneye duck. In the spring of 1961, with the support and encouragement of George Waterston (of the RSPB) and Colonel Grant, I put up some duck nestboxes for goldeneye around Loch an Eilein and other places in Strathspey. We watched and waited and everything but goldeneyes nested in the boxes: tawny owls, pied wagtails, redstarts, jackdaws and others. It was tremendously disappointing.

In July 1970, a birdwatcher from England visiting Lochan Mhor saw a goldeneye duck with four ducklings. This was the first recorded breeding of wild goldeneyes in Britain, although of course, they may have nested many centuries ago before records began. From that time, the bird has increased quite dramatically.

Goldeneyes lay large clutches of eggs and sometimes younger females lay in the same boxes as older birds. The most eggs I have recorded in a nest box was

28, and 21 chicks were reared out of that box. No wonder their numbers went up from three pairs in 1973, to 41 by 1981. Nowadays there are about 150 pairs in Badenoch and Strathspey, and they have spread to other parts of the Highlands. It is heartening to think that it all started at Rothiemurchus.

In the nineteenth century, a variety of song birds increased in Strathspey; they included tree pipits, redstart, mistle thrushes and wood warblers. More recently, garden warblers have increased but the willow tit became extinct after the severe winters of the 1950s. Some species occasionally reach this far north and can be persuaded to colonise. Pied flycatcher was one such species. David Pierce lived on Rothiemurchus in the 1970s and put up nest boxes for pied flycatchers. They increased until there are now about a dozen pairs nesting annually. Rothiemurchus has also provided nesting habitat for very rare species attempting to colonise Scotland from Scandinavia. Three pairs of wrynecks nested in 1968, and have occasionally bred since, and redwing have bred also. They choose places like Rothiemurchus because they provide conditions most similar to the species' normal breeding range in the boreal forests of Sweden and Norway.

So the bird scene is very interesting and special. It has changed; it is different to two hundred years ago, but the key species are still here and it is still a very special place for birds and for ornithologists.

We now see lots of red deer, but it is important to remember that red deer were absent from Rothiemurchus and elsewhere on the northern slopes of the Cairngorms two hundred years ago. They had been hunted to local extinction. I believe that Rothiemurchus was made a sporting 'deer forest' in 1843 and a few years later some deer calves were brought from the Forest of Mar in Deeside. A woman looked after them on a croft near Loch an Eilein; her neighbours complained because the tame deer calves would jump up on the peat stacks and knock them over.

There were none in Abernethy Forest at that time either, and Smith, the famous hunter of Rynuie in Tulloch, used to go all the way to the Forest of Mar to get a deer for the pot in the old days, so it is wrong to think they have always been here in the same numbers. These introduced animals provided the nucleus for the recovery of the deer herds and by 1896, 92 stags and 54 hinds were taken for sport on Rothiemurchus.

There are roe deer, mountain hares, stoats and weasels. Some of them have shown a decline over the years, and some of them have increased, or even returned after decades of absence like the pine marten. Some were new arrivals, like the brown rat and the house mouse, followed by the rabbit in the eighteenth century. The hedgehog was probably a newcomer as the forest declined and agricultural land increased. More recently, the American mink arrived due to escapes from fur farms. It is now well established and is regarded as a pest.

At the start of this millennium, and certainly at the start of the previous one, nine big mammals are likely to have been present in Rothiemurchus but eight of them became extinct. Five were herbivores: wild boar, beaver, elk, wild cattle and reindeer. Wild cattle, wild boar and beaver were crucial to forest ecosystems and it is difficult see how the natural forest ecosystems of the future can work properly without these mammals.

Table 2: List of mammals of Rothiemurchus

Hedgehog, mole, common shrew, pygmy shrew, water shrew, Daubenton's bat, long-eared bat, pipistrelle bat, brown hare, mountain hare, red squirrel, bank vole, field vole, water vole, brown rat, wood mouse, house mouse, fox, stoat, weasel, American mink, pine marten, otter, badger, wild cat, red deer, roe deer.

Extinct species: polecat, wild cattle, beaver, brown bear, wolf, lynx, wild boar, reindeer, elk.

The brown bear and the lynx were brought to extinction early on but the wolf clung on until more recent times. The last Scottish wolf was allegedly killed nearby in the Findhorn gorges in 1743, and probably the last in Rothiemurchus not many years before that.

One large mammal of the original nine remains and it is man, the most successful of the lot. Colonel Grant was renowned for his attitude towards some tourists, but I must place on record my worry about the increasing penetration of wild places crucial to sensitive wildlife by large numbers of people. They have little realisation that they are damaging wild nature.

These people often criticise others in the countryside who damage or destroy wildlife through their landuse activities, without recognising that their leisure activities may also being causing change and damage. Of course, some creatures become tame and accept food from visitors, but eating scraps from tourists is not the same as living in a natural ecosystem. I sometimes like to remind people of the present American view that in wild land a 'fed animal' is ultimately a dead animal. We will need to care for our most treasured nature areas better in the future.

Acknowledgements

I owe a debt of gratitude to the late Colonel Iain Grant who was so helpful and enthusiastic towards me when I first visited Rothiemurchus, and to John and Philippa Grant for their friendship and for continued permission to traipse around a most beautiful part of our planet.

Selected Bibliography

Baxter, E.V. & Rintoul, L.J. 1953. *The Birds of Scotland*. Edinburgh.
Brown. P. & Waterston, G. 1962. *The Return of the Osprey*. London.
Dennis, R. 1984. *Birds of Badenoch & Strathspey*. Inverness.

Dennis, R. 1991. *Ospreys*. Lanark.

Dennis, R 1995. *Birds of Badenoch & Strathspey*. Grantown-on-Spey.

Gordon, S. 1925. *The Cairngorm Hills of Scotland*. London.

Harvie-Brown, J.A. & Buckley, T.E. 1895. *A Vertebrate Fauna of the Moray Basin*. 2 Volumes. Edinburgh.

Jenkins, D. 1988. *Land Use in the River Spey Catchment*. Aberdeen.

Nethersole-Thompson, D. 1951. *The Greenshank*. London.

Nethersole-Thompson, D. 1966. *The Snow Bunting*. London and Edinburgh.

Nethersole-Thompson, D. 1973. *The Dotterel*. London.

Nethersole-Thompson, D. 1974. *Pine Crossbills*. Berkhamstead.

Nethersole-Thompson, D. & Watson, A. 1974. *The Cairngorms*. London.

Ritchie, J. 1920. *The Influence of Man on Animal Life in Scotland*. Cambridge.

Thom. V. 1986. *Birds in Scotland*. Calton.

Waterston, G. 1971. *Ospreys in Speyside*. Edinburgh.

5. In Search of Wilderness, Nature and Sport: The Visitor to Rothiemurchus 1780-2000

Robert A. Lambert

Of all the districts overshadowed by the extensive Cairngorm range the most magnificent, by universal consent, is Rothiemurchus. It is a region entirely unique ... A day here in October is something to be remembered all one's life, when the tops of the mountains all round the horizon are pure white with the early snow, and their slopes are adorned with the brilliant tints of faded bracken, golden birch and brown heather, and all the low grounds are filled with the unchangeable blue-green of the firs (Macmillan 1907:3-4).

With such descriptive prose Hugh Macmillan began his 1907 book entitled *Rothiemurchus*; his own written tribute to a landscape of forest and loch (illustrated with photographs by W Dempster and Clarence Kerr) that had been conceived as he dwelt amongst the Scots pines in his 'forest cabin', in the very heart of Rothiemurchus. Macmillan's book pays homage to the late-Victorian fashion for appreciating and writing about landscape and the natural world. In a series of chapters that cover parts of the estate as diverse as Glen Einich, Loch an Eilein and the lands that border Kinrara, he offers the reader confirmation that all the components necessary to compose the most picturesque and sublime landscape image, and hence aesthetic appreciation of a view, are to be found in the sweeping vistas of Rothiemurchus. In a sense, this is the 'prose of human adoration', topographical worship of a landscape that is all Nature, primitive, savage and unredeemed and yet full of suggestion for the contemplative and poetic mind. 'Rothiemurchus,' Macmillan believed, 'lays its solemn spell upon the spirit like the aisles of a cathedral ... its stillness is awe-inspiring ... it is not solitude, but the presence of some mystery – some supernatural power' (Macmillan 1907:22–23). Macmillan's view covers both history and geography, as well as the romantic and spiritual needs of humankind in the face of such natural beauties. Few have described so well the interplay of Scots pine and birch in the Rothiemurchus scene:

They are seen to best advantage when struggling out of the writhing mists that have entangled themselves among their branches; and no grander background for a sylvan scene ... no fairer subject for an artist's pencil exists in Nature. While the rain brings out the fragrance of the weeping birches ... that are the embodiments of the feminine principle of the woods, it needs the strongest and hottest sunshine to extract the pungent, aromatic scents of the sturdy firs, which form the masculine element of the forest (Macmillan 1907:17).

However, in Macmillan's eyes all was not well in this 'most beautifully balanced' landscape picture. During the summer months, tourists and picnickers cluttered the scene, and at Loch an Eilein 'crowds of visitors who come from all parts of the country in carriages and on bicycles,' brought an unwelcome human presence into this 'special show-place of the district.' Even worse, the rail station at Aviemore had become the gateway to Rothiemurchus, and now 'innumerable trains in the summer months pass north and south, and passengers from all parts of the world meet each other on the platforms' (Macmillan 1907:8,27–53). Yet what Macmillan was observing was nothing new; there had been a tradition of coming to Rothiemurchus that could be traced back to the last two decades of the eighteenth century (although visitors were not very numerous then) and Macmillan himself was a part of that visitor tradition, no matter what he was seeking.

5.1: Visitors gazing at Loch an Eilein Castle and the loch, perhaps hoping to see an osprey.
Photograph: J E A Steggall, July 1901, Neg. 21.12.
By kind permission of the University of St Andrews Photographic Collection

Mrs Murray of Kensington

Perhaps the most remarkable traveller to have come to the lands of Rothiemurchus across any century, was the Honourable Mrs Murray of Kensington. She came in 1796, and travelled alone with no thought for her personal safety, although she did make use of hospitality from friends of friends in the north. She stands in time as an exceptional, pioneering lady of travel, possessed of a critical eye in the observation of the scenery through which she journeyed, and a prodigious recorder of the detail of accommodation standards on the route, grand views and the health of Highland estates. Witness her first sight of Rothiemurchus on the 1796 tour:

> On the opposite side of the river stands Rothamurchus, beautifully situated, bounded by crags, and near the river's edge. The crags around Rothamurchus are covered with wood, and the verdant meads are ornamented with fine trees; and the house is within sight of Cairngouram mountains, whose hollow cliffs are filled with never-melting snow (Murray of Kensington 1799:212).

On her 1796 visit she stayed in the inn at Aviemore and although charmed by the view from there, found the filth and smoke in the house quite unbearable: '...It was impossible to breakfast at Aviemore Inn...' she complained. On her second night at the inn she could not sleep and confided that it was the worst inn (except the King's House on the Glen Coe road) that she had ever visited: 'All out of doors, however, is beautiful.' Few have been charmed by Aviemore itself, even in the 1790s. Mrs Murray returned to Rothiemurchus in 1801 for two weeks and spent sometime at the Doune with Jane, Duchess of Gordon and Lady Georgina, 'scrambling awhile in this bewitching sylvan scene'. It was on this second extended visit that Sarah Murray offers her most informative and entertaining descriptions of the estate, even going on to offer any future single lady travellers in the area a comprehensive list of 'friendly gentlemen in that district.' Mr Grant was included on the list, as was a Mr Osburn from Hull who rented a cottage in the summer months over at Glenmore. There was obviously building work going on at the Doune during her visit, for Murray noted that, 'Mr. Grant is building a house, which, when finished, will be an excellent one. The proprietor and his lady have great taste ... it will be one of the most desirable properties (in point of beauty) in the Highlands. It is not a very extensive estate, but it is *multum in parvo*'. Murray also noted the extremely fine echo off the Loch an Eilein castle walls, thrilled at a ride up Glen Einich where she tumbled from her horse ('it has the wildest rocks and mountains about it I ever saw'), found Loch Gamhna to be 'beautiful', and urged the visitor to seek out 'a cluster of small lakes in the midst of the firwoods'. She rode on Mr Grant's pony up onto the Cairngorm plateau, while 'the gentlemen walked', mused on the beauty of ptarmigan in flight and, 'rode through Glenmore and entered the firwoods of Rothiemurchus, which are in extent 16 square miles...' Sarah Murray wrote much about the state of the Rothiemurchus woods and became unexpectedly attached to them:

> The grandeur and sublimity of such venerable extensive woods cannot be conceived, when the eye has been accustomed only to plantations of firs; and till I saw the natural growth of pines in the Loch Leven Glen, Braemar, Rothiemurchus and Rannoch, I disliked a fir wood excessively, which from

stiffness, is quite the reverse of picturesque. Mr. Grant annually cuts down, perhaps £1,500 worth of timber; and yet, when riding through his woods, not a tree to the eye is missing (Murray of Kensington 1803:64–66,341–350).

In the early 1930s, H V Morton revelled in her enthusiasm and energy 'With the eye of a hawk and the campaigning spirit of Hannibal plus Caesar plus Napoleon, she drove her coach right into and over the Highlands; and nothing could frighten or deter her or blunt her stupendous curiosity ... What a woman!' (Morton 1933:295). My sentiments exactly.

Colonel Thomas Thornton

At the start of the nineteenth century the visitor to the lands of Rothiemurchus was most likely to be a sportsman or traveller-adventurer, a pioneer upon whose subsequent observations and descriptions of landscape and plentiful game a fledgling Highland tourist industry would base itself. Colonel Thomas Thornton of Thornville Royal was perhaps the best known of these earliest visitors and led the English sporting invasion into the Highlands of Scotland, especially of Badenoch and Strathspey. The date of Thornton's 'Sporting Tour' has never been precisely known, although it is now commonly accepted as having taken place in 1786, with a brief reconnaissance trip to Inverness-shire in 1783 or 1784 (where he perhaps first made the acquaintance of the laird of Rothiemurchus). Colonel Thornton's place in the development of field sports in Great Britain is assured, for he was a falconer of some repute, enjoyed running with the hounds, was a keen fisherman and was a prodigious athlete who enjoyed a sporting bet (Brander 1964:119–140). The journal of his 'Sporting Tour' was not published until 1804 and characteristically was prone to exaggeration and lapses in factual detail. It received a vitriolic review from a young lawyer named Walter Scott in *The Edinburgh Review*, who found the Colonel to be the natural enemy of good taste, scandalous in his behaviour towards women, wholly unsporting in his treatment of game (Scott was particularly concerned with the 'childish' and 'murderously bloody' activity of falconry) and prone to describe topography using plagiarised phrases from Thomas Pennant and Thomas Gray. Scott found the book boring, 'because it contains a long, minute and prolific account of every grouse or blackcock which had the honour to fall by the gun of our literary sportsman – of every pike which gorged his bait – of every bird which was pounced by his hawks – of every blunder which was made by his servants – and of every bottle which was drunk by himself and his friends' (Scott 1804/5:400). Despite such critical tirade, Thornton does offer a unique if eccentric view of Rothiemurchus in the late eighteenth century, from the visitors' point of view. He certainly liked what he saw, although he felt that,

> Mr. Grant of Rothemurcos has built a very commodious house, not in the best situation, though his table is the most enviable in the world, as is his estate (Thornton 1804:179).

Colonel Thornton was much taken with the scenic beauty of Loch an Eilein (Loch Neiland, as he spelt it), and thus stands as a direct forerunner of the many Victorian travellers who would gather at this part of Rothiemurchus Estate to find tranquillity and seclusion. Witness Thornton:

> ... to the north is a forest composed of firs and junipers, and filled with roebucks and stags, whose foliage may well be said, by its thickness to be impenetrabile nullo astro as is the delightful Glenmore, where, I believe, the trees are still larger than Rothemurcos forest. So highly were we pleased with this heavenly scene, the very finest I think in Scotland, that we did not regard its growing late. In fact, it is such a charming spot, that I must strongly recommend it to all travellers into these parts; and to ladies as well as gentlemen (Thornton 1804:97–98).

He was similarly charmed by the view from 'Avemore' where 'the opposite hills are covered, almost to the very skies, with immense forests of fir, and Glenmore and Rothemurcos woods, about seven or eight miles broad and twelve or fourteen long, give a melancholy shade to the pearl-coloured mountains around them' (Thornton 1804:107). Thornton did venture onto the high tops up through Glen Einich, and he noted 'ptarmigant' ('but here they swarm'), although he was more concerned with the reaction of his travelling party to the immensity of the Cairngorm scene:

> It is impossible to describe the astonishment of the whole party when they perceived themselves on the brink of that frightful precipice, which separated them from the lake below! They remained motionless a considerable time, equally struck with admiration and horror (Thornton 1804:91).

On the shores of Loch Insh, Thornton mused on what was necessary for the full enjoyment of a glorious visual scene, and concluded that it depended upon who was in your party, the nature of the weather, 'and finally on the sensations of the admirer, who will perceive, more or less beauties, according as those sensations are, or are not, in unison with the scenery ...' (Thornton 1804:157). Returning that day to Rothiemurchus, he felt that 'no effect of art can possibly equal this terrestrial paradise ... we preceeded on, scarcely speaking.' The laird of Rothiemurchus gave a goshawk to Colonel Thornton as a gift, the bird having been taken from the forest of Rothiemurchus in which there were a 'few eyries in the great fir-trees, some of which [he] saw' (Thornton 1896:vii). Thornton's final recommendation to future travellers to the region was to undertake the horse ride from 'Pitmain and Avemore' into the heart of Rothiemurchus, 'from thence get a guide to Loch Neiland, which again turns off the road to the right, a mile on this side of Rothemurcos, and I pronounce this to be one of the very first rides in the world' (Thornton 1804:98).

Sir Herbert Maxwell, in his introduction to the 1896 Sportsman's Library edition of the 'Sporting Tour' believed that if the credit for opening up the Highlands to the ordinary tourist is given to Walter Scott, then 'Colonel

Thornton ... anticipated him in disclosing their unsuspected attractions for the sportsman ... the wealth of sport opened to the travellers, the freedom to angle, shoot and hawk where and when they pleased ... must have rendered their progress one to be vastly enjoyed.' Maxwell also took offence at Scott's review over ninety years earlier, believing...

> ...the Colonel's quick observation, general culture and love of nature enabled him to write a book which can be read with interest even at this distance of time, for it will be found to contain a great deal more than a monotonous record of the slaughter of wild creatures ... at the same time, the Sporting Tour might not have been nearly such interesting reading if it had been of a quality to earn higher praise from him [Scott] (Thornton 1896:v, xii-xiv).

From Colonel Thornton then we have some of the finest topographical descriptions of Rothiemurchus in the 1780s, and often this aspect of his writing is ignored. Undoubtedly, he was a cavalier and brash individual and the 'arrival of the Colonel and his friends must have struck the natives as the descent of a little army, and the cavalcade, as it wound its way among the hills, must have created quite a sensation' (Bulloch 1931:6). The Colonel journeyed into Badenoch carrying a precious load of perch in a kettle with which he hoped to stock the local lochs, including those at Rothiemurchus. This introduction scheme met with certain logistical problems, and the Colonel sought local help:

> The kettle having been found very inconvenient, on account of the water splashing out at every jolt ... I wished to hire a person to carry it on foot ... I proposed it to several peasants, but taking advantage of our necessity, they had the conscience to ask me eight days wages (Thornton 1804:67–70).

On then into Rothiemurchus went this colourful retinue with a peasant carrying a kettle of perch. Thornton toured France in 1802 during the Peace of Amiens and often compared the afforested landscape to what he had seen in the Highlands of Scotland, especially in the Grampians (Thornton 1806). He retired to France in 1815 after a series of legal battles (Anon 1801) and died in Paris in March 1823, but his story was resurrected in the middle of the twentieth century by Michael Brander who set off 'On the Trail of Colonel Thornton' across Great Britain in 1959. Brander met with Lieutenant-Colonel J P Grant of Rothiemurchus who was just about to depart the estate to visit St Kilda and Fair Isle, but both men had the time to agree that Colonel Thornton was probably the biggest sporting liar unhung (Brander 1973).

Other Sporting Visitors

Writing in 1931, John Bulloch sensed that Colonel Thornton had to fight with Colonel George Gordon of Invertromie and Charles Fyshe Palmer (MP for Reading) to gain a sporting foothold in Badenoch and to curry favour with the

Grants of Rothiemurchus. At the end of the eighteenth century, obtaining a suitable property in the area to rent during the sporting season was a pressing concern for a visiting sportsman in an expanding and competitive lease market. In September 1794 George Gordon wrote from Killiehuntly of his plans for the coming week:

> We shall take a ride to-morrow ... and fish Loch Guinach on Tuesday, and I hope to reach Kinrara on Wednesday, fish with Rothiemurchus on Friday, and start for Gordon Castle about Tuesday sen'night... (Bulloch 1931:13).

Around 1794, Charles Palmer was renting a house at 'Kennakyle' (Kinakyle, near Craigellachie) and was caught in a rent dispute with Grant of Rothiemurchus, whom he referred to in a letter to William Tod (the Duke of Gordon's factor in Lochaber and Badenoch) as 'a damned rogue'; Palmer was later in trouble with the Duke for illegal hunting of roebuck in 'Glenmoor'. The dispute with the laird of Rothiemurchus seemed to rumble on for some years and centred on the sale of furnishings and the price of corn in transactions between the two protagonists (Bulloch 1931:17–23). These legal disputes between the estate owners and sporting tenants were not unusual, especially in an era when a good deal of profit could be made from the sporting visitor and his retinue in the local provision of accommodation, the hire of horses and guides and the sale of foodstuffs from the estate.

Rothiemurchus became a deer forest in 1843 and shortly afterwards the laird introduced some red deer from Mar, releasing them into the woods near Loch an Eilein. Over the course of the nineteenth century, Badenoch and Strathspey became less isolated, and the sporting visitor could enjoy easier access to estates such as Rothiemurchus from improvements in the carriage roads north, and in the 1860s by the development of the rail line north from Perth to Inverness (Nethersole-Thompson and Watson 1974; Grant 1980:11–14). Elizabeth Grant has written a great deal about the many visitors who came to stay or dine at the Doune of Rothiemurchus, and of how it was accepted custom that neighbouring estates would accommodate some sporting guests during the busiest autumn weeks on Rothiemurchus when the Doune was full. Naturally, the Grants reciprocated this hospitable gesture to help out other local lairds and their families. Reading *Memoirs of a Highland Lady*, one gets the impression that Elizabeth Grant found these many visitors to be, on the one hand, an exciting influx of personalities and viewpoints, but also somewhat of a 'necessary curse' to be endured:

> Visitors poured in as usual; no one then ever passed a friend's house in the highlands, nor was it ever thought necessary to send invitations on the one part, or to give information on the other; the doors were open literally, for ours had neither lock nor bolt, and people came in sure of a hearty welcome and good cheer (Grant of Rothiemurchus 1992:214).

When the Duchess of Bedford rented the Doune while the Grants were on colonial service in India, Edwin Landseer made a number of visits, and sketched at various locations on the estate; these drawings are now in the possession of the Duke of Hamilton (Black 1996; J P and P Grant *pers comm*). Tracing the written records and observations of the various shooting tenants of Rothiemurchus across the nineteenth century is an arduous and often fruitless task for the historian. We are, therefore, forced to rely on incidental references provided in published texts, or information that can be gathered from reading between the lines in relevant archival letters or communiqués. In such a fashion, it is known that Lord Stamford held the shooting tenancy of Rothiemurchus in 1872 and mistakenly shot an osprey as it rose from the ground on a lochside; he was supposedly haunted by his 'trigger-happy' conduct that day, for some years to come (Brown and Waterston 1962). In 1898 the annual sporting rent of Rothiemurchus deer forest was advertised at £1,750 with fishing and shooting rights. Guests stayed in Drumintoul Lodge on the estate, which had been built in 1878, and contained four public rooms, twelve family bedrooms and eight servants' bedrooms. There was even a tennis lawn. Game was to be taken 'in a fair and sportsmanlike manner' (SRO;NRA 102:483).

The enduring popularity of Rothiemurchus to the sporting visitor lasted well into the first four decades of the twentieth century. Some visitors were not afraid to offer constructive advice to the laird on how the sport could be improved, especially for the fisherman. Hector Burn-Murdoch wrote from Duns in Berwickshire in September 1927:

> We enjoyed our pike outings on Loch an Eilein ... and as to stocking L an E, you have an accomplished hatchery in Loch Gamhna. I wonder if you could devise a means of catching the little fellows wholesale and dumping them in Loch an Eilein.

Burn-Murdoch wrote again in November, '... I feel that Loch Gamhna needs if possible a great reduction of the numbers of little fish to begin with. If you could introduce a few really large trout they might cannibalize successfully. Next, a good food supply...' One wonders how the Grants reacted to such meddling (albeit well-intentioned) in the running of the estate. That people did visit from the southern part of England is shown in this letter from Melplash in Dorset, dated April 1928:

> ... I imagine Col. Grant is again giving tickets to fish this year on the Spey. I hope to be at [the] Station Hotel, Aviemore beginning of May. Would he feel inclined to let me the stretch on the Spey for May 1st - May 16th? (SRO; NRA 102:401).

The Nineteenth-Century Traveller

Following in the footsteps of the earliest travellers into the northern Highlands in the second half of the eighteenth century – men such as Thomas Thornton, Thomas Pennant and Edward Burt (Youngson 1974; Smout 1983; 1991) – came a new wave of adventurers, travellers and investigators, who did not just focus on the sporting benefits of the Highlands but sought to understand the manners and the customs of the people they encountered as well as to describe the landscapes through which they passed. Over the course of the nineteenth century, and especially after the 1870s, these travel writers would become an integral part of the late Victorian tourist discovery of regions such as Strathspey; up to about 1830, few travellers cared to venture past the romantic scenery of Highland Perthshire which was believed to represent the most magnificent and picturesque scenery in Scotland (see Macculloch 1823). They came north to search out, 'the simple magnificence of nature, exhibiting in sublime variety her stupendous monuments,' that visual balance and symmetry between the stark nakedness of the hills and the sublime beauty of the woods that clothed them. Some could also write in the words of a late twentieth century 'get away from it all' mentality:

> They left without sorrow to its anxious inhabitants the ceaseless noise of carriages, the continual movement of busy feet and of feverish tongues, and those harassing tumults of the breast, which produce great wealth and splendour, but neither contentment nor gratification... (Mawman 1805:6,124).

John Macculloch, writing in the 1820s, found Kinrara to be more beautiful than neighbouring Rothiemurchus, although the pinewoods of the latter were of note, when investigated in close detail. Macculloch made an interesting observation: that to wander in Rothiemurchus or the 'great and noble Glenmore' was akin to wandering in 'an American forest' due to the amount of timber extraction work being undertaken. He described Loch an Eilein as, 'a fir lake ... the only very perfect example in the country' (Macculloch 1824:396–401). Writing about Strathspey in its entirety in 1848, Robert Somers felt that 'fertility and barrenness are here seen in closer contiguity than in other districts.' For the Improving-minded Somers there was too much wasteland in the region, so 'that a deep stratum of wretchedness lies under this fair exterior' (Somers 1848:28–38). George and Peter Anderson in mid-century produced a guide book that painstakingly described all facets of the Badenoch landscape from the marshes at Insh, the birchwoods at Craigellachie and the views from Aviemore. They warned their readers that the Cairngorm area was not well known, 'only of late years ... [by] a comparatively small number of adventurous tourists', and that the 'fastness cannot be explored, except by dint of a complete fagging day of resolute walking.' Rothiemurchus came in for special aesthetic praise: '...proceeding now from the ferry at Rothiemurchus ... we must not omit to visit Loch-an-Eilein ... but the lake, its castle, and its woods, recall to the imagination rather the things we read of in the novels of the Otranto school than a scene in real life...' (Anderson and Anderson 1850:285,288). Peter Anderson returned to Rothiemurchus in July 1863 and stayed at the Doune as a guest of William P Grant of Rothiemurchus. He found much to interest his ornithological and botanical mind, thought the contrast between the low ground and the high tops on the estate to be dramatic, and thrilled at the mix of birch and Scots pine in the many views: '... filled up with birch and a pine forest, where the young trees and the old wood – a remnant of the once great forest – most pleasingly intermingle their contrasted light and dark livery with that of the birch. Altogether the whole scene is very grand indeed' (Anderson 1903). These sentiments were echoed by A E Knox who came to Rothiemurchus in a series of consecutive autumns from 1865 to 1868. Troubled by gnats and his lack of success at shooting a roebuck, Knox sought solace in the feeding antics of a party of crossbills in a tree above his head, and the balance between forest, loch and mountain in the Cairngorm landscape when seen with the eye of an artist:

> ... farther off the woods of Rothiemurchus clothing the hills in the middle of the picture, which, as the view recedes, becomes higher and higher, until the eye rests at last on the dark belts of perenially green pine forest, and beyond these again the irregular outline of the Grampians encloses the distant landscape (Knox 1872:3).

In 'Hints for the Vacation Ramble' serialised in 1881, an 'Old Tramp' urged that visitors to the Cairngorms should approach the mountains from the Rothiemurchus side, for although it was possible to reach the high tops by 'the valley of the Dee,' this could involve 'the risk of intrusion on the sorely beset privacy of Royalty – a peril which every loyal and even humane subject ought dutifully to shun' (Anon 1881:174). Over a century later the rambler in the 1990s can plan a route through Rothiemurchus using the walking guides written by Ernest Cross (Cross 1992; 1993; 1994).

Loch an Eilein and its Ospreys

In the second half of the nineteenth century, the Victorian tourist saw Loch an Eilein as the most attractive and interesting part of Rothiemurchus, and this was in part due to the residency of a pair of nesting ospreys on the ruins of the castle in the middle of the loch; the presence of the birds and their fishing expeditions in the loch seemed to add an ornithological charm to the whole vista. There was nothing unusual about the castle nest site at Loch an Eilein as ospreys also nested in the nineteenth century on Ardvreck Castle on Loch Assynt, at Kilchurn Castle on Loch Awe, on a ruined building on an island in Loch Lomond and on an old shooting lodge at Loch Morlich. What was different, though, in the case of the Loch an Eilein nest, was that it was readily visible from the shore of the loch, and was so well known to visitors that its history was compiled by C G Cash and published in popular natural history and hillwalking journals with a wide readership (Cash 1903; 1914). Successive Grant lairds sought to offer protection to the ospreys in both the nineteenth century, and in the late 1950s when the birds recolonised Speyside. In April 1893, the Zoological Society of London awarded silver medals to both Donald Cameron of Lochiel and John Peter Grant of Rothiemurchus, 'in recognition of the efforts made to protect the ospreys in their respective districts.' The medal was designed by Landseer. In October 1960 the RSPB bestowed their silver medal upon Lt-Colonel J P Grant of Rothiemurchus to mark the first successful breeding of the ospreys in 1959 under RSPB protection, and because the laird had helped with night-watches of the nest at Loch Garten (Waterston 1966:19). Ospreys then were good for tourism even in the nineteenth century; visitors came to Rothiemurchus to see the birds, and some written records of their observations exist. William Jolly (HM Inspector of Schools) visited Loch an Eilein in 1879 and 1880 and was much taken with the estate and the ospreys: '...And it certainly was a romantic and impressive scene not easily forgotten, to be seated there by the shores of one of the most alpine and solitary of lakes, amidst the venerable remains of the Caledonian forest of yore ... Go to Rothiemurchus if you want to feel the dignity and power of what vegetable life may become, even under our northern skies' (Jolly 1879:5). Jolly had much to say about the state of the trees in the surrounding woods, but was also moved to pen a stinging attack on the irresponsible sporting visitors (in this case Lord Stamford) and egg collectors who continually put the future of the nest in jeopardy. Stamford was criticised thus: 'when a noble Lord, it seems, inspired by the noble British tendency "to kill something", amidst even the grandest scenes of nature, shot one of the birds.' Jolly had hoped to be fortunate enough to see the osprey 'stoop to catch a fish', but missed out on this aspect of osprey behaviour, and so continued to lambaste those who would shoot such birds or steal the eggs for a collection.

> Nothing too severe can be said in reprobation of such wanton slaughter of the wilder inhabitants of our hills and moors, and especially of the insensate and heartless destruction of our rarer animals ... the arm of the law should be invoked to declare it criminal so to indulge their savage propensities in thoughtless itch for notoriety, or for the possession of a rarity (Jolly 1879:5).

Around 1880 the laird of Rothiemurchus had decreed that visitors were not allowed to use a boat on Loch an Eilein in case they forced the ospreys to desert the nest, but much of the damage done to the species in Scotland by egg collectors had been perpetrated in the 1840s and 1850s. More often than not these visitors came under the cover of darkness to raid the nest. Sometime before 1843 and his departure for southern Africa, Roualeyn Gordon-Cumming robbed the nest. Lewis Dunbar visited the estate in 1848 and took three eggs from the nest; in 1849 he took another three eggs which he sent to Charles St. John in Sutherland, and spent some hours skulking around Loch Gamhna looking for another nest to rob. Dunbar returned in 1850 to take a further three eggs which he sent to John Hancock in Newcastle; in 1851 he sent two eggs from the Loch an Eilein nest to John Wolley and a further three eggs in 1852. This annual pilfering would have continued had Dunbar not had the good sense to emigrate to Australia in 1853, no doubt much to the delight of the Grants and all others who sought to protect the breeding ospreys at the loch (Brown and Waterston 1962; Dougall 1978:177–178). Although Jolly's 1879 article is in praise of the osprey, a week after its publication in *The Scotsman*, an irate letter from an early nature conservationist living in Edinburgh drew attention to Jolly's foolhardiness in broadcasting his observations and memories:

> I write ... to remonstrate with the author of the communication for giving the name of the locality of the breeding place of any rare bird. The writer seems interested in the preservation of the osprey, a bird equally innocent and interesting, yet he has taken the surest means for its destruction by publishing to the world the definite information he has given.

This anonymous correspondent, signing only as 'S', felt that the protection of these birds should be the responsibility of the estate owners; 'the eyrie of an eagle or an osprey should now be regarded by the owners of estates as one of the heirlooms they have to be proud of' (Anon 1879:3). C G Cash was another who disliked the hunting, shooting and fishing fraternity (Anon 1917), and found in the ospreys at Loch an Eilein a sense of the spirit and serenity of the natural world, in the face of so much human indifference to the suffering of wild creatures. He was aware too of why the ospreys were so popular with visitors:

> There is, perhaps, no other of our raptores at once so interesting and so easy to observe. The dark, stern golden eagle will not brook observation, but sails off indignant on majestic wing; the smaller falcons and hawks dart in arrowy flight from the presence of man. But the Osprey allows of moderately near approach, and permits itself to be inspected as it stands or sits on its nest, or as it soars in wide curves above the loch (Cash 1903:125).

Cash made observations of the Rothiemurchus ospreys from 1894 to 1903, believing that the birds 'add such a charm to that most beautiful of Highland beauty-spots, Loch an Eilein.' The archives of the Grants of Rothiemurchus also contain letters written by visitors to the laird about osprey sightings on the estate in the last decade of the nineteenth century (SRO;NRA 102:337). Just as Victorian visitors watched the osprey fishing in Loch an Eilein, so the birdwatcher or tourist of the 1990s can still watch these birds fishing in that loch, or sit in a specially built hide at the fish farm at Inverdruie where the Speyside osprey population regularly fishes in the summer months. Ospreys remain an integral part of the visitor experience at Rothiemurchus. The tenor of the nineteenth century was the persecution of birds of prey across Scotland; Rothiemurchus is a rare example from that century of the site of a nesting bird of prey being admired and preserved, and symbolises the beginning of our attempts to conserve the osprey.

Naturalists, Photographers, Mountaineers and the Martineau Family

Across the nineteenth and twentieth centuries, a wide range of 'specialist interest' visitors have come to Rothiemurchus to engage in the amateur or professional pursuit of their chosen field. Foremost amongst these visitors have been naturalists. As early as June 1771, the botanist James Robertson came to observe and record the principal plants growing in 'the parish of Rothymurcus', which he found contained an 'abundance of excellent Fir and Birch, together with some Hazle and Poplar,' and on 'a small lake called Lochnaisland at the head of this wood, there is an isle' which 'abounds with Toothwort' (Henderson and Dickson 1994:167–169). Over a hundred years later, George Carpenter and William Evans came to Rothiemurchus in the summer of 1893 to list the spiders to be found on the estate; the 'fine forests of Rothiemurchus, Glenmore and Abernethy' were said to 'possess a rich spider fauna' (Carpenter and Evans 1894:227). In classic and often pioneering studies, more celebrated naturalists such as John Harvie-Brown, T E Buckley and Henry Tegner have focused on the vertebrate fauna to be found on the estate, in an effort to understand the ecology of the area, and their published works contain an element of topographical observation, species history and distribution information and extracts from communiqués with other distinguished naturalists on the topic of the fauna of Rothiemurchus (Harvie-Brown and Buckley 1895; Tegner 1971). Throughout his life, and especially when he lived at Achantoul in Aviemore, Seton Gordon was a regular visitor to Rothiemurchus and had a particular friendship with Iain Grant that was based around a shared love for piping and ornithology (Eagle 1991:241–242). On leave from the RAF in June 1942, E H Ware came to Rothiemurchus to catch up with birds that are unique to the Caledonian pine forest and the high tops, species that all English-based birdwatchers must eventually come north to get on their treasured lifelists. Ware failed to see a capercaillie and left slightly disgruntled, but little has changed in the ensuing fifty years. The modern birder, armed with telescope and binoculars comes to Speyside and enters Rothiemurchus just to see those same species (crested tit, Scottish crossbill, black grouse, capercaillie, ptarmigan and dotterel), and quite often finds that the forest hides the resident 'capers' rather too well (Ware 1946). One advantage that the modern ornithologist does have is a plethora of site guides that try to offer geographical help in the location of key species; even Britain's top twitcher Lee Evans has realised that all birders must eventually head for Rothiemurchus (Gooders 1977:281, 286; Evans 1996:82, 96, 225, 242; Dennis 1995). In 1952, Desmond Nethersole-Thompson prepared a survey of the birdlife of Rothiemurchus, and George Waterston was a regular visitor in the middle decades of the twentieth century (Waterston 1950). Birds have endured as the most popular aspect of natural history on the estate, attracting not only amateur and professional field naturalists, but also photographers.

As early as 1895, O A J Lee photographed the osprey nest at Loch an Eilein, and over the next sixty years George Kearey, the Kearton brothers, Arthur Brook, George Yeates, Christopher Mylne and Eric Hosking all were drawn to Rothiemurchus to photograph birds. Stuart Smith famously captured crested tits on film in Rothiemurchus in 1940; the attic at the Doune holds two signed and framed photographs of a Scottish crossbill and hen capercaillie taken on the estate in 1952 by John Fisher (Hosking and Lowes 1947; Lambert 1996:75,80 and *pers obs*). From the landscape photographic archives that exist it is also possible to learn that an individual photographer such as J E Steggall made photographic tours to Rothiemurchus in 1893, 1901 and 1922 and that the bulk of Robert Adam's landscape photography in Rothiemurchus took place from 1924 to 1956, made easier by his retirement to Kingussie in 1949; the Burn-Murdoch stereoscopic slides of Rothiemurchus were taken by the Edinburgh solicitor and amateur photographer from 1924 to 1937 (Lambert 1996:74–80; The Photographic Collections of the University of St. Andrews, and the University of Dundee).

5.2: Access through Rothiemurchus and Glenmore up onto the high tops.
Photograph: J E A Steggall, August 1901. Neg. 21.37 'Cairn Gorm – on the way up'.
By kind permission of the University of St Andrews Photographic Collection

In the thirty years before the First World War, Rothiemurchus was used as a gateway to the Cairngorms by the mountaineering clubs that had established themselves in the 1880s and 1890s in the north-east and Central Belt towns.

This first wave of climbing clubs (the Cairngorm Club and the Scottish Mountaineering Club), had a predominantly middle class and professional membership; the more egalitarian climbing clubs, with a student and working class affiliation, would not come until the 1930s (Weir 1985; McNeish and Else 1994). Even the most brief research in the many editions of the *Cairngorm Club Journal* and the *Scottish Mountaineering Club Journal* will reveal many written memories of walking excursions and climbing trips to the Cairngorms that contain observations of Rothiemurchus, noted as the club members passed through on their way to the high tops. E P Buchanan found the 'variety of scenery and beauty of colour' to be the charm of Rothiemurchus in 1915; in 1903, William Smithard found Loch an Eilein to be 'perfectly beautiful' and the forest of Rothiemurchus to be 'immense ... looking very dark in spite of brilliant sunshine'; in 1920, G Murray Lawson confided that to write of his beloved Cairngorms was 'a labour of love' and that within them, the forest of Rothiemurchus inspired a feeling of freedom and space, and adorned with its rich colouring brought on contemplation and introspection: '... our recollections of that day are now a happy memory' (Lawson 1920; Smith 1890; Smithard 1903; Buchanan 1915; Backhouse 1913; Frere 1953; Robinson 1931; Russell 1928; Clark 1922; Beattie 1922). Rothiemurchus hosted an era of genteel recreation in the years of seemingly endless summers from 1880–1910, but that was all to radically change in the inter war years and under a new age of mass recreation and the motor car. In the last years of the 1890s, R Bruce Lockhart recalls halcyon childhood summers staying with his grandmother at Inverdruie House and bathing nude in the Spey and the Druie; the shooting tenant at the Doune was Lord Manvers (Bruce Lockhart 1937:167–177).

The growth of interest in climbing and hiking in Scotland from the middle of the nineteenth century brought the rights of way and access debate in the countryside into the public arena. The Scottish Rights of Way Society (which, under a different name, dates back to 1847) found themselves in perpetual conflict with the lairds of Rothiemurchus from around 1882 until 1904 over 'the unwarrantable shutting up of old Footpaths and Drove Roads'. The Society first sought to erect guide posts for walkers on paths across the estate in 1885, but the posts were quickly removed and the Loch an Eilein gate locked by estate staff. After years of legal debate and petition, by 1903 the Grants of Rothiemurchus chose to admit the existence of some paths and driving roads, but visitors were excluded from the forest each year during the shooting season from 12 August to 13 October. It appears as if the access debate to the lands of Rothiemurchus had calmed down by 1925, as the Society could proudly claim that four new iron guide posts were to be put on the estate, and no opposition to this was expected from the landowner (SRO; GD335–1,22,56). The Scottish Rights of Way Society had an unusual ally in this battle for Rothiemurchus from the 1880s, in the shape of James Martineau, the Unitarian minister, educator and philosopher who came with his family to holiday at the Polchar perhaps first in 1876; this cottage became the Martineau family summer home for the next fifty years which they leased from the Grants living just a quarter of a mile away at the Doune. Right under their Grant hosts' noses, the Martineau family behaved like fifth columnists on the estate from 1882, writing scandalously rude letters about the laird, bribing estate staff and even getting their daughters to pull gates off their hinges in 1885. They were still committing minor acts of sabotage on the estate and reporting every action that the laird took to Society headquarters in Edinburgh in 1904. Tolerance of unruly intellectual guests must be a Grant virtue.

5.3: The General Rice Memorial, Loch an Eilein. A hapless visitor to Rothiemurchus. The engraving reads: 'This stone was erected by the people of Rothiemurchus in affectionate remembrance of Major General Walter Brook Rice, late Royal Artillery, who was accidentally drowned while skating near this spot, 26 December 1892.' Photograph: J E A Steggall, April 1922, Neg. 40.3.
By kind permission of the University of St Andrews Photographic Collection

As regular summer visitors, the Martineaus' did give much of worth to the parish. Mary Ellen Martineau established a local library for the benefit of Rothiemurchus and district, and Edith and Gertrude Martineau taught some handicrafts (wood carving) to the local people for almost twenty-five years

(SRO;GD335–22 and Martineau Monument *pers obs*). From Gertrude we have some wonderful descriptions of late Victorian holidaymakers misbehaving themselves around the shores of Loch an Eilein; she complained that so many who came to visit did not appreciate the place and they 'began to do mischief':

> As the carriages passed under the trees the people laid hold of the boughs and tore them off and flung them on the road; they threw stones at the squirrels and screamed to each other across the loch; the men sang rude songs and the shouting to the 'old man in the castle' became ... common and ... noisy (Scarlett 1988:47–66).

One wonders what Miss Gertrude would think of modern day Aviemore!

The Motor Car and the Visitor, 1930–1950

Visitors had come to Speyside by rail from the middle of the nineteenth century, and the scenic view from Aviemore station gained much fame with holidaymakers. In the first half of the twentieth century, the world of the Speyside holiday changed dramatically, with the new era of popular Highland tourism being fuelled by better roads, improved rail access and increased leisure time. The motor car, coach and omnibus gave a new sense of personal freedom. Motoring enthusiasts subscribed to the *SMT Magazine*, which offered both advice on car purchase and gave numerous suggestions for motoring holidays in Scotland. May Lawrence and her family recorded how they had come north from London in 1935, 'to breathe the air among these wonderful old Scots pines ... of Rothiemurchus and Glenmore' (Lawrence 1936:41). Articles that fondly recalled a visit to Rothiemurchus, especially Loch an Eilein, were commonplace, and it made no difference to the enthusiasm of the prose if the writer had journeyed by car or motor coach (Murdoch 1936; Anon 1937; Macartney 1934; Anon photograph 1947). It had been the rapid increase in motor transport on the main north road to Inverness, via Pitlochry and Aviemore, that had led to improvements on the road in the 1920s, as part of a comprehensive scheme for Highland roads proposed by Inverness County Council; the road was widened and resurfaced, an awkward bend at the Slochd was rectified and some blind corners were removed (Grant 1980:17).

The summer of 1934 saw unprecedented numbers of holidaymakers using the Highland roads, and they were celebrated as 'very ordinary folk', reclaiming their right to admire Scotland's landscape: 'the liberation of the weekend crowd has come to stay,' wrote Moray Maclaren that year (Maclaren 1934). Charles Plumb, writing in 1935, found Aviemore to be 'a wretched place ... a mere line of petrol pumps and tin shops planted on the side of the Great North Road'. These commentators were, after all, hillwalkers and ramblers who had come to the Cairngorms to escape, for a time, an urban lifestyle, to exercise body and mind. Plumb urged the outdoor enthusiast to seek spiritual refreshment by staying overnight at Coylumbridge, a 'pretty village ... air rich with the pines,' as close as one could to Rothiemurchus; an overnight stay in Aviemore, he felt, drained the 'self-sufficiency of health and strength which comes of having given yourself to the wilds and allowed yourself to forget the dismalities of organised society' (Plumb 1935:70–71). Holiday guidebooks from this era stress how beautifully the woods of Rothiemurchus fit into the visual panorama, when seen against the backdrop of the Cairngorm mountains (Quigley 1949:17–21; Batsford and Fry 1948:18), and were often illustrated with landscape and natural history photographs taken by the likes of Robert M Adam and V A Firsoff (Lambert 1996; Firsoff 1965). Even in the 1930s, there was a delightfully wicked fashion for contrasting the ugliness of Aviemore with the natural beauties of Rothiemurchus, with some writers being scarcely able to believe that the two could exist in such close proximity. Witness Matt Marshall:

> ... Down and down I strode by the footpath ... until immediately below and flooding the wide plain, rolled the green sea of the Forest of Rothiemurchus ... I exulted in its breezy openness, in its cool greenness, in the wildness of its heathy glades, ferny hollows, and banks of bog-myrtle. Thankfully I plunged into it and let its dark green tide close over me ... For I was tired of the cold hills ... I was sick of the heights (Marshall 1933:168).

And now his scathing view of the neighbouring town: 'Here I did not stay long. Aviemore is merely a one-horse hamlet where motorists pull up to fill up, and is noted chiefly, if it is noted at all, for the number and excellence of its automatic chocolate machines' (Marshall 1933:172).

Of course, as critical a visitor as Wilfred Taylor would never be pleased with the scenery of Rothiemurchus, confessing 'as it happens I am not an impassioned lover of the upper Spey Valley ... I find the atmosphere peculiarly neutral and at times gloomy and oppressive. The Monadh Ruadh are not very theatrical mountains and they are too far from the sea ...' (Taylor 1955:11).

The Doune of Rothiemurchus Hotel 1935–1942

Sometime in the 1880s the Doune of Rothiemurchus appears to have been a Victorian commercial hotel, catering no doubt to holidaymakers who wished to enjoy a combination of romantic Highland scenery, some sporting endeavour with gun or rod, mountaineering or golf and a dose of invigorating exercise in clean fresh air (SRO; NRA 102:483). This was just a decade before the first publication of *Memoirs of A Highland Lady* under John Murray in 1898, so the estate would not have the literary allure of the former residence of Elizabeth Grant, as it would when the Doune was next a hotel in the late 1930s.

In 1981, an Edinburgh legal firm deposited in the SRO a ledger, some day books and trading and profit accounts relating to the Doune of Rothiemurchus in the late 1930s and the early part of the Second World War, and from these documents a history of the hotel venture has been constructed (Calvert and Lambert 1997). It is apparent that a lease was negotiated for the use of the house as a hotel, probably between the major provider of the initial monies for the venture, John Johnson, and Colonel Grant of Rothiemurchus. R T Bowyer was taken on as manager of the hotel from January 1935. It has been estimated that it had around 23 rooms, and was open to guests from April to October. Most visitors came in July, August or September each year (SRO; GD387/11–2,3) although some income was also derived from the provision of chance meals to passing holidaymakers, in an age of the widening ownership of motor cars. Some visitors brought their own staff with them. The hotel management advertised the venture in newspapers as wide afield as the *Inverness Courier*, *Yorkshire Post*, *Dundee Courier* and *Glasgow Herald*; they also displayed an attractive sign on boards at Aviemore rail station, and were members of the Scottish Travel Association; advertisements were also placed in the *Scottish Ski Club Journal*. Perhaps the biggest blow to the success of the hotel came because of the failure of the Doune of Rothiemurchus Hotel to be listed in the Scottish Motor Traction Co. Ltd Magazine (SMT) 'Directory of recommended British Hotels' which began in April 1934. Newspaper adverts for the hotel tended to focus on the location of the house, as in this advert for April 1936 in *The Scotsman*: '...a Mansion House ... beautifully situated in 17 acres of Parkland on the banks of the River Spey.' Additional attractions were listed as, 'Home Farm Produce, free fishing, near golf course and tennis courts, mountaineering'. The car-borne tourist was obviously the key visitor, with the hotel describing itself as an 'excellent centre for motoring'. As the summer of 1936 progressed, the advert changed, this time to make more of the beauty of the pine forest on the estate. The terms were described as 'moderate', with the hotel 'beautifully situated ... near Rothiemurchus forest in the Cairngorms.' The hotel also produced an attractive tariff brochure with a photograph of the Doune and an accompanying direct quotation from *Memoirs of A Highland Lady* which spoke of Elizabeth Grant's visual impressions of her 'beloved duchus' in the summer of 1812, as she returned there from England. It was as if the tourist in the 1930s was making the journey of 1812 with Elizabeth Grant, and her literary association with the house no doubt enticed many well read visitors to holiday on the estate. The Doune of Rothiemurchus Hotel closed for business in 1942, irreparably damaged by the collapse of the domestic tourist industry in the opening years of the Second World War (Calvert and Lambert 1997:164–166; J P and P Grant *pers comm*).

The Cairngorms National Nature Reserve 1954–1975

The fledgling Nature Conservancy in Scotland declared the Cairngorms NNR on 9 July 1954 in Edinburgh, and a formal Nature Reserve Agreement was signed between the NC and J P Grant of Rothiemurchus later in that month, pertaining to the parts of Rothiemurchus Estate that fell within the declared boundaries. It was the largest nature reserve in Britain extending to 39,689 acres. Visitor management was not high on the list of priorities for the NC and much of the early work on the NNR concentrated on climatalogical and Scots pine regeneration research; the first *Management Plan* of 1959 for the NNR makes little mention of public access to the reserve. The NC failed to take into consideration the long tradition of recreation in the Cairngorms and on Rothiemurchus, and made no formal provision to regulate access or guide visitors, and were thus caught off-guard by the sheer popularity of the reserve; by 1962 they could barely cope. The reserve created in 1954 as a 'living laboratory' was becoming a popular playground for visitors seeking healthy recreation in an attractive Highland setting with relatively easy transport access. It would be as late as 1964 before the NC sought to confront the visitor issue on the NNR; visitor surveys were undertaken at Loch an Eilein in 1964 and 1965, signposting was debated as an answer and the provision of nature trails was mooted. Rothiemurchus was recognised throughout these two years of discussion as the most popular and easily regulated visitor gathering area on the NNR, and it was decided therefore to make Loch an Eilein the focus for future concentrated visitor management efforts from 1965 onwards. The NC opened a Nature Trail around the loch in June 1965 and it proved a successful venture with around 30,000 visitors having used it by 1969. By 1970, there is a sense that the laird of Rothiemurchus was beginning to feel that providing visitor information and guidance via reserve leaflets and nature trails was becoming obsolete, and so he offered the NC the use of an old cottage on the Rothiemurchus Estate, near the limekiln adjacent to Loch an Eilein, to convert into a formal visitor reception centre. The Loch an Eilein Visitor Centre was finally opened on 1 July 1972 by Sir Frank Fraser Darling, with an associated exhibition entitled 'The Native Pinewoods' (Crumley 1991; Weir 1953; Archives of the NC Aviemore at Achantoul). H M Steven and A Carlisle investigated the extent and health of the native pinewoods of Scotland from 1950 to 1956, and they probably visited Rothiemurchus a number of times from their base in Aberdeen during those six years. They wrote with the scientist's eye about the forest at Rothiemurchus, describing its size, levels of natural regeneration, its tree and shrub species and the vertebrate and invertebrate life within the pinewoods (Steven and Carlisle 1959:120–125).

Visitor Management 1975–2000

In 1975 the visitor management strategy at Rothiemurchus was changed and the estate developed a far more active and professional approach to the provision of visitor services that identified customer demand and aimed to satisfy it. Writing in 1990, the present laird of Rothiemurchus described this as:

> We create an awareness of the quality of experience that can be obtained so
> that visitors can sensibly decide on whether or not to visit Rothiemurchus.
> There is no point in attracting people who would be happier elsewhere (Grant
> of Rothiemurchus 1990:51).

This shift in emphasis came about because the development of Loch an Eilein as a 'honeypot area' for visitor reception had proved unworkable and unmanageable. A passive approach to visitor management on the estate in the 1950s, 1960s and early 1970s (without a commercial angle) had not worked. Visitors felt unguided in their appreciation of the estate's natural heritage and in reaction to that were prone to create disturbance to wildlife, drop litter, light forest fires, and camp within the estate boundaries. Some dogs ran out of control and regular acts of vandalism against both trees and estate buildings occurred (Grant of Rothiemurchus 1990:51).

A Ranger Service was established in 1975, along with a programme of guided walks running from April to September that attracted around 90 people in 1976. In June 1978 the first Visitor Guide was published by the estate and was seen to have an important publicity role; the guided walks programme was expanded, but it was felt that there was a growing demand from the visiting public for more ecological interpretation and identification to be included in the service. 1978 also saw the development of a commercial Farm Tour on the estate, conveying visitors by tractor and trailer across two farms, for a walk amongst the pedigree herd of Highland cattle and around the older farm steadings; 212 people paid for this experience in its inaugural year. The *Annual Report* for 1978 also makes mention of the Ranger Service's wider community role, in that efforts should be made by the estate to establish contacts between itself and local and regional schools and education-orientated organisations (Rothiemurchus Estate *Annual Reports* 1975–1978).

By 1982 the estate staff had noticed an enormous reduction in the number of annual 'incidents' that related to a poor public understanding of the recreational and ecological resource they were using. Typical incidents included unauthorised camping, the lighting of fires and dogs running out of control; the Ranger Service was obviously proving its worth:

Year	Total Number of Incidents Reported
1976/77	757
1977/78	839
1978/79	556
1979/80	495
1980/81	277
1981/82	226
1988	75

(Rothiemurchus Estate *Annual Reports* 1976–1988).

Litter has remained a constant management headache over the decades, and visiting youth organisations using the Loch an Eilein campsite regularly help estate staff in clearing up any rubbish left lying about. A second shift in emphasis in the provision of visitor services by the estate came in 1985, when the performance of the Ranger Service over the previous decade was examined in detail next to the expectations of the modern visitor. The *Annual Report* for 1984/85 noted that visitor numbers had increased dramatically, and that this trend was expected to continue into the late 1980s, especially during the summer and autumn months. In 1975 when the Ranger Service had been established, 'it was only necessary to replace the private signs with a welcoming sign system, and supervise the public in a benign and chatty matter, for the Service to be appreciated.' Everybody, and every form of recreational pursuit now wanted its own space in the countryside, and a different type of visitor could now be expected on the estate. The Ranger Service was to become even more professional and visible:

> The public have also changed in that they expect improved standards, litter-free footpaths, the availability of the Ranger in person all the time, and now to a limited extent, they don't mind paying for guided walks, tours, car parking and they usually want to buy something to take home
> (Rothiemurchus Estate *Annual Report* 1984/85:2).

Rothiemurchus Estate also took over the operation of the popular Loch an Eilein Visitor Centre in 1985 along with the nearby lavatories. This centre had previously been run by the NCC during the summer months and the estate in the winter (when the NCC did not have the finance to keep it open). Although 1985/86 was dominated by uncertainty created by the protracted renewal negotiations between Rothiemurchus Estate and the NCC over the Cairngorms NNR Agreement (which had expired in June 1984), the estate did introduce one innovation in the visitor management strategy. Total visitor numbers to the estate at all locations were now estimated according to the 'take up of our free Visitor Guide and footpath map,' and signatures in the Visitors' Book and on-the-spot observations and counts by estate staff. In the late 1980s the estate could expect annual visitor numbers to be in the 280,000 region; in 1987, about 5,165 people paid to go on a farm tour, a bird walk or a deer walk. By 1989 over 327,100 were visiting the estate on commercial excursions or just for recreational pleasure; Rothiemurchus Visitor Centre at Inverdruie was recording around 86,000 people per year, with about 80,000 visiting Loch an Eilein (Rothiemurchus Estate *Annual Reports* 1985–1989). In the 1990s annual visitor numbers have fluctuated between 290,000 and 330,000, and in 1990 the estate developed corporate entertainment facilities that sit well alongside the trained Ranger Service. The estate now has an estimated 50km of footpaths that are open all year round, although from the winter of 1984 the estate staff have been concerned that both walking and cross-country skiing during the winter tends to accelerate footpath erosion; much of this unseasonal use stems from frustrated skiers who have been turned away from Cairn Gorm due to the over-crowding problems which exist there on some weekends.

Over the last twenty years numerous special events have been held at

Rothiemurchus, ranging from sponsored walks through the Lairig Ghru, orienteering events, the popular Rothiemurchus Highland Games (which attracts 5,000 visitors every August), sheepdog trialing and winter dog-sled racing, undoubtedly reflecting the wide diversity of recreational activities that now bring people into the countryside in increasingly large numbers. In the 1990s, the Grant family hospitality has a strong commercial element but that financial factor has ensured that the estate has survived in the second half of the twentieth century under single family ownership, where so many Highland estates have fallen to foreign owners or have been sold on over and over again. The vision for the twenty-first century is tied up in an Access Project initiative (at its first draft stage in the Spring of 1997) which aims to continue to consciously improve the visitor's quality of experience on the estate, to protect the environment and to ensure that there is no damage to local community interests. In this balancing act, the estate plans to offer the new technological visitor access to a wide range of scientific, literary, historical and archaeological information about the lands of Rothiemurchus, which the Ranger Service will be trained to interpret (J P Grant *pers comm*). A 'Highland Lady' tour that includes a visit to the Doune was instigated in 1993 and could profitably be expanded along both academic, interpretative and commercial lines.

In the Spring of 1996, John Grant of Rothiemurchus spoke of the modern challenge of visitor management on his estate to a Grampian TV crew filming a documentary entitled 'Managing the Wilderness'. Visitor numbers were about right, he explained:

> What really matters is the quality of the experience, and of course it gets much more difficult to give a good quality of experience, the more people that there are. So we wouldn't hope that visitor numbers necessarily go up here at Rothiemurchus, but what we are hoping is that people have a really good time when they are here; they get to see what is really important about Rothiemurchus and enjoy it and understand it, and remember it, and tell their friends about it (J P Grant: Interview, Grampian TV *Managing the Wilderness*, 1996).

Conclusion

To the above vision for the future we can now add the human angle, which was provided in 1996 most eloquently by the Empire historian Thomas Pakenham who came to Rothiemurchus to 'meet with a remarkable tree'. Pakenham believes that too few historians pay homage to Britain's rich legacy of ancient trees, 'these ancient living documents' (Wavell 1996). He goes on to chide us for our complacency and express the sense of an intertwined destiny between mankind and trees. With only a short accompanying text to each photograph, he gives us a visual stimulus and many fresh emotional and spiritual reasons why we should cherish these trees (Pakenham 1996:32-35). The future for

Rothiemurchus is not just about preserving its glorious natural heritage for its own sake, but also for what so many people come to seek, or feel or to witness as they wander amid the Scots pines on the estate. Eric Fitch Daglish sought to capture this 'sense of belonging' in his botanical guidebook to Britain in 1929:

> Love of the countryside, with the myriad beauties of its ever varying moods, is inborn in the majority of mankind, and however rare may be the opportunities offered of gratifying the desire to live in close or intimate contact with wild nature, few of us are debarred from spending brief periods of hours or days, from time to time, amid the joys of the open air (Daglish 1929:5).

Historically, recreation on the lands of Rothiemurchus has not solely been about mere exercise for human legs; it has had a strong mental, spiritual and visual component for two centuries now, but we are only just coming to recognise this. After all, wilderness is not about an absence of people from the landscape; it is defined by a particular philosophical relationship that we have with the natural world, that sees humans as partners in a wider community of living things.

Acknowledgements

The author would like to thank the following people for their help:

Mr and Mrs J P Grant of Rothiemurchus who provided historical information and were generous with their hospitality; Chloë Randall and Samantha Faircliff of the Rothiemurchus Estate Staff; David Calvert; Christopher Smout and Margaret Richards of the Institute for Environmental History at the University of St Andrews; Peter Moore of SNH Aviemore; Dick Balharry of SNH; Pat Whatley and Jennifer Tait of the University of Dundee, Department of Archives; the staff of the University of St Andrews, Rare Books and Photographic Collections; Kim Macpherson; my mother and father who first brought me to visit Rothiemurchus as a child.

Abbreviations used in the text

NC	Nature Conservancy
NCC	Nature Conservancy Council
NNR	National Nature Reserve
RAF	Royal Air Force
RSPB	Royal Society for the Protection of Birds
SMT	Scottish Motor Traction Co. Ltd
SNH	Scottish Natural Heritage
SRO	Scottish Record Office, Edinburgh
NRA (S)	National Register of Archives (Scotland)
GD	Gifts and Deposits

Bibliography

Archival Material

The archive of the Grants of Rothiemurchus is catalogued in the SRO in Edinburgh under NRA(S) 102, but the archive is privately held at the Doune of Rothiemurchus, Inverness-shire. Permission must be sought to consult it. The archive of the Scottish Rights of Way Society is held in the SRO under GD335.

The relevant archives of the Nature Conservancy and Nature Conservancy Council are in part held at the SNH Aviemore office at Achantoul, but are uncatalogued and in some disarray. The archive of the Doune of Rothiemurchus Hotel is held in the SRO under GD387/11.

Photographic Archives

Archival photographs of Rothiemurchus can be found in the University of St Andrews Photographic Collection: The Steggall Collection, The Robert M. Adam Collection, and The Valentine Collection. In the University of Dundee Photographic Collection: The Alexander Burn-Murdoch Stereoscopic Slide Collection MS 104.

Rothiemurchus Estate

The Annual Reports of Rothiemurchus Estate from 1976 to 1996 were consulted.

Television

J P Grant of Rothiemurchus was interviewed as part of the Grampian TV documentary 'Managing the Wilderness' broadcast in 1996.

Secondary Sources

Anderson G, Anderson P. 1850. *Guide to the Highlands and Islands of Scotland Including Orkney and Zetland, Descriptive of their Scenery, Statistics, Antiquities and Natural History ...* Adam and Charles Black, Edinburgh.

Anderson P. 1903. 'Memoranda of An Excursion to the Grampians and Strathspey in July 1863' in *Cairngorm Club Journal*, Volume 4, No. 21, July, pp 156–166.

Anon. 1801. 'Law Report' in *London Times*, Monday 29 June, No. 5145, p3.

Anon. 1879. 'The Osprey' in *The Scotsman*, June 12, p3.

Anon (an Old Tramp). 1881. 'Hints for the Vacation Ramble' in *Blackwoods Edinburgh Magazine*, No. DCCXC, Volume CXXX, August, pp 173–174.

Anon. 1917. 'Obituary – C.G. Cash' in *Scottish Geographical Magazine*, Volume 33, pp 465–466.

Anon. 1937. 'A Day's Run – to the Majestic Cairngorms' in *SMT Magazine*, Volume 19, No. 3, September, no page numbers.

Anon photograph. 1947. 'Loch an Eilean, Rothiemurchus' in *Take Note*, October, p9.

Backhouse E. 1913. 'Midnight Wanderings In The Larig' in *Scottish Mountaineering Club Journal*, Volume 12, No. 71, June, pp 286–290.

Batsford H, Fry C. 1948. *The Face of Scotland* B.T.Batsford, London. First published in 1933.

Beattie AB. 1922. 'A Day On Braeriach' in *Scottish Mountaineering Club Journal*, Volume 16, No. 94, October, pp 174–181.

Black D. 1996. 'Duty to the Duchus' in *Country Living*, No.121, January, pp 66–69.

Brander M. 1973. *A Hunt Around the Highlands – On the Trail of Colonel Thornton* The Standfast Press, Gloucs. First Published in 1961.

Brander M. 1964. *The Hunting Instinct: The Development of Field Sports over the Ages* Oliver and Boyd, Edinburgh.

Brown P, Waterston G. 1962. *The Return of the Osprey* Collins, London.

Bruce Lockhart RH. 1937. *My Scottish Youth* Putnam, London.

Buchanan EP. 1915. 'Through Rothiemurchus to Rebhoan' in *Scottish Mountaineering Club Journal*, Volume 13, No.77, June, pp 251-258.

Bulloch JM. 1931. *Sporting Visitors to Badenoch* Highland Handbook V, Robert Carruthers, Inverness.

Calvert D, Lambert RA. 1997. 'A Highland Hotel Venture: the Case of the Doune of Rothiemurchus Hotel, 1935–1942' in *Northern Scotland*, Volume 17, pp 153-172.

Carpenter GH, Evans W. 1894. 'A List of Spiders Collected in the Neighbourhood of Aviemore, Inverness-shire' in *Annals of Scottish Natural History*, No.12, October, pp 227-235.

Cash CG. 1903. 'The Loch-an-Eilein Ospreys' in *Cairngorm Club Journal*, Volume 4, No.21, July, pp 125-131.

Cash CG. 1914. 'History of the Loch An Eilein Ospreys' in *Scottish Naturalist*, No.31, July, pp 149-158.

Clark WI. 1922. 'Reminiscences of the Cairngorms' in *Scottish Mountaineering Club Journal*, Volume 16, No.93, April, pp 109-116.

Colonel Thornton T. 1804. *A Sporting Tour Through the Northern Parts of England, and Great Parts of the Highlands of Scotland...* James Swan, London.

Colonel Thornton T. 1806. *A Sporting Tour Through Various Parts of France in the Year 1802* Longman, Hurst, Rees and Orme, London.

Colonel Thornton T. 1896. *A Sporting Tour through the Northern Parts of England, and Great Parts of the Highlands of Scotland* Edward Arnold, London. This edition edited by Sir Herbert Maxwell for The Sportsman's Library.

Cross EL. 1992. *Walks In the Cairngorms – Near Aviemore* Luath Press, Barr. First published in 1984.

Cross EL. 1993. *The Speyside Holiday Guide* Luath Press, Barr.

Cross EL. 1994. *Short Walks in the Cairngorms* Luath Press, Barr. First published in 1991.

Crumley J. 1991. *A High and Lonely Place – The Sanctuary and Plight of the Cairngorms* Jonathan Cape, London.

Daglish EF. 1929. *Our Wild Flowers and How to Know Them* Thornton Butterworth, London. First published in 1923.

Dennis R. 1995. *The Birds of Badenoch and Strathspey* Colin Baxter Photography, Grantown-on-Spey.

Dougall R. 1978. *A Celebration of Birds* Collins and Harvill Press, London.

Eagle R. 1991. *Seton Gordon – The Life and Times of a Highland Gentleman* Lochar, Moffat.

Evans LGR. 1996. *The Ultimate Site Guide to Scarcer British Birds* LGRE Productions, Amersham.

Firsoff VA. 1965. *On Ski in the Cairngorms* W. and R. Chambers, Edinburgh.

Frere RB. 1953. 'A Cairngorm Odyssey' in *Scottish Mountaineering Club Journal*, Volume 25, No. 144, April, pp 124-131.

Gooders J. 1977. *Where to Watch Birds* Pan Books, London. First published in 1967.

Grant IF. 1980. *Along a Highland Road* Shepheard-Walwyn, London.

Grant of Rothiemurchus J. 1990. 'Managing Rothiemurchus Estate' in Conroy JWH, Watson A, Gunson AR (eds) *Caring for the High Mountains – Conservation of the*

Cairngorms Centre for Scottish Studies, Aberdeen.

Grant of Rothiemurchus E. 1992. *Memoirs of a Highland Lady – Volumes I and II* Canongate Press, Edinburgh. First published in 1898.

Harvie-Brown JA, Buckley TE. 1895. *A Vertebrate Fauna of the Moray Basin – Volumes I and II* David Douglas, Edinburgh.

Henderson DM, Dickson JH (eds). 1994. *A Naturalist in the Highlands– James Robertson: His Life and Travels in Scotland, 1767-1771* Scottish Academic Press, Edinburgh.

Hosking E, Lowes H (eds). 1947. *Masterpieces of Bird Photography* Collins, London.

Jolly W. 1879. 'Loch-an-Eilein and its Ospreys' in *The Scotsman*, 9 June, p5.

Knox AE. 1872. *Autumns on the Spey* John Van Voorst, London.

Lambert RA. 1996. 'Strathspey and Reel: Photography and the Cairngorms' in *Inferno: the St. Andrews Journal of Art History*, Volume III, pp 68-81.

Lambert RA. 1998. 'The history of nature conservation and recreation in the Cairngorms, 1880-1980', unpublished PhD thesis, Institute for Environmental History, University of St Andrews.

Lawrence M. 1936. 'Aviemore Amid the Pines' in *SMT Magazine*, Volume 16, No.4, April, pp 40-43.

Lawson GM. 1920. 'The Cairngorms – An Appreciation' in *Scottish Mountaineering Club Journal*, Volume 15, No.89, April, pp 233-240.

Macartney WN. 1934. 'The Central Highlands and the Coasts of Lorne' in *SMT Magazine*, Volume 12, No.6, June, pp 106-115.

Macculloch JD. 1823. *A Description of the Scenery of Dunkeld and Blair in Atholl* Joseph Mallett, London.

Macculloch JD. 1824. *The Highlands and Western Isles of Scotland, Containing Descriptions of their Scenery and Antiquities...* Longman et al, London.

Maclaren M. 1934. 'The Freedom of the Countryside – Scotland and the Motor Age' in *SMT Magazine*, Volume 13, No.6, December, pp 54-56.

Macmillan H. 1907. *Rothiemurchus* JM Dent and Co., London.

Marshall M. 1933. *The Travels of Tramp-Royal ...* W.M. Blackwood, Edinburgh.

Mawman J. 1805. *An Excursion to the Highlands of Scotland, and the English Lakes, with Recollections, Descriptions and References to Historical Facts* T. Gillet, London.

McNeish C, Else R. 1994. *The Edge – One Hundred Years of Scottish Mountaineering* BBC Books, London.

Morton HV. 1933. *In Scotland Again* Methuen, London.

Murdoch ML. 1936. 'In the Heart of the Cairngorms – through Glen Einich with a Camera' in *SMT Magazine*, Volume 17, No.2, August, pp 45-48.

Murray of Kensington S. 1799. *A Companion and Useful Guide to the Beauties of Scotland....to Which is added, A more Particular Description of Scotland, Especially That Part of it Called The Highlands* George Nicol, London.

Murray of Kensington S. 1803. *A Companion and Useful Guide to the Beauties in the Western Highlands of Scotland, And In the Hebrides... To Which is added, A Description of Part of the Main Land of Scotland...* W. Bulmer and Co., London.

Nethersole-Thompson D, Watson A. 1974. *The Cairngorms – Their Natural History and Scenery* Collins, London.

Pakenham T. 1996. *Meetings With Remarkable Trees* Weidenfeld and Nicolson, London.

Plumb C. 1935. *Walking In the Grampians* Alexander Maclehose, London.

Quigley H. 1949. *The Highlands of Scotland* BT Batsford, London. First published in 1936. With photographs by Robert M. Adam.

Robinson DW. 1931. 'Ghosts' High Noon on the Cairngorms' in *Scottish Mountaineering Club Journal*, Volume 19, No.112, November, pp 261-265.

Russell AW. 1928. 'Some Memories of Braeriach' in *Scottish Mountaineering Club Journal*, Volume 18, No.106, November, pp 214-219.

Scarlett MH. 1988. *In the Glens Where I was Young* Siskin, Milton of Moy.

Scott W. 1804/5. 'Article XI – Colonel Thornton's Sporting Tour' in *The Edinburgh Review (or Critical Journal)*, Volume V, October-January, pp 398-405.

Smith WA. 1890. 'The Cairngorms in Summer' in *Scottish Mountaineering Club Journal*, No.3, September, pp 106-114.

Smithard W. 1903. 'First Impressions of the Cairngorms' in *Cairngorm Club Journal*, Volume 4, No.21, July, pp 143-148.

Smout TC. 1983. 'Tours in the Scottish Highlands from the eighteenth to the twentieth centuries' in *Northern Scotland*, Volume 5, No.2, pp 99-121.

Smout TC. 1991. 'The Highlands and the Roots of Green Consciousness,1750-1990' in *Proceedings of the British Academy*, Volume 76, pp 237-264.

Somers R. 1848. *Letters from the Highlands: The Famine of 1847* Simpkin, Marshall and Co.,Glasgow.

Steven HM, Carlisle A. 1959. *The Native Pinewoods of Scotland* Oliver and Boyd, Edinburgh. The 1996 edition is by Castlepoint Press, Dalbeattie.

Taylor W. 1955. *Scot Easy – Travels of a Roads Scholar* Max Reinhardt, London.

Tegner H. 1971. *A Naturalist on Speyside* Geoffrey Bles, London.

Ware EH. 1946. *Wing to Wing – Birdwatching Adventures at Home and Abroad with the RAF* The Paternoster Press, London.

Waterston G. 1950. 'Mountain Bird-Watching' in *Scottish Mountaineering Club Journal*, Volume 24, No.141, April, pp 316-320.

Waterston G. 1966. *Ospreys in Speyside* RSPB, Edinburgh.

Wavell S. 1996. 'Under the spreading chestnut, oak, elm, yew...' in *The Sunday Times – Books*, 20th October, pp 8-9.

Weir T. 1953. 'Why Not Rothiemurchus – A Cairngorm Nature Reserve' in *Scots Magazine*, Volume LX, No.2, November, pp 134-135.

Weir T. 1985. *Tom Weir's Scotland* Penguin Books, Harmondsworth. First published in 1980.

Youngson AJ. 1974. *Beyond the Highland Line – Three Journals of Travel in Eighteenth Century Scotland* Collins, London.

6. The History of the Rothiemurchus Woodlands

Chris Smout

As we have learned from GWS Barrow (see Chapter 1, above), written records relating to the forests at Rothiemurchus go back into the Middle Ages, but it is only from about the middle of the seventeenth century that the records at the Doune become plentiful enough to tell anything like a continuous story.

It divides into three parts. First, in the century and a half from about 1650, exploitation of the woods was dominated by two things. One was the spasmodic attempt – usually by outsiders, sometimes by the laird's family – to exploit the woods by reaching a southern market. These efforts failed to bring sustained profit to anyone, and probably had little impact on the woods. The other was the continuous trafficking in wood by local people, either buying from the laird or, more probably and commonly, operating under licence from the laird and selling on, down-river or overland. This exploitation succeeded. It was sustainable, but it is likely to have had a substantial effect on the structure and character of the wood.

The second period was the nineteenth century, characterised by spasms of heavy exploitation by the landowners or their creditors, including one or more episodes approaching clear fell, but also accompanied by the first efforts of the owners to protect the forest from domestic stock. At this time local people had no stake in the forest except as employees – lumberjacks, hauliers, sawyers or floaters – and the marketing of the wood was in the hands of the estate.

The third period is since 1914 when, apart from episodes of felling in the two world wars, the emphasis has been on conservation. This was true both before and after the establishment of the Cairngorms National Nature Reserve, of which the woodlands form an important component.

The emphasis in this chapter will be on the first two periods (subdividing the second), partly because we are all more familiar with the recent past, and partly because it is difficult yet to get an appropriate research perspective on the present century.

The Late Seventeenth and Eighteenth Centuries

The Rothiemurchus pines were already familiar to the outside world and utilised for the market at the beginning of this period. An account of the parish of Rothiemurchus produced for Sir Robert Sibbald around 1682 speaks of a sawmill and a 'great Firr Wood of two miles in length, but very broad', and one for the adjacent parish of Duthil speaks of the population neglecting working the land, 'being addicted to the Wood which leaves them poor'.[1] The situation in Strathspey was probably much as in Glen Tanar, Glen Carron, on upper Deeside and in other places where local people gained part of their living from cutting deals and spars in the woods and floating them down river or taking them by horse to the nearest market.

The first outsider who thought he might turn a penny from the woods was an Englishman, Benjamin Parsons, described initially as a merchant of Aberdeen and doubtless an incomer with the Cromwellian Union, who in 1658 secured interests both in Rothiemurchus and in Abernethy. In Rothiemurchus he obtained a lease of 'the whole fir woods' for thirteen years, with permission to build sawmills on the local streams. By 1664 Parsons had taken over the whole of Abernethy, and was also described as master of the sawmill at Garmouth. By 1671 he had acquired additional interests at Kincardine and even at Glencalvie in Ross-shire, and was building a ship at Garmouth, no doubt from Strathspey pine. Nevertheless, he was soon in deep financial trouble, pursued for outstanding debts by the laird of Grant in 1669, and by the laird of Rothiemurchus and Dr Samuel Collins of London in 1671. Next year he is described as a merchant of Leith and nothing further is heard of him in the north. It remains a mystery how much timber he was able to extract from Rothiemurchus in his thirteen-year tack, but there is no evidence that it was a vast amount.[2] Rothiemurchus wood was purchased for repairs to the tolbooth at Nairne in 1673, so the withdrawal of Parsons from the scene did not bring trade to an end.[3]

Immediately after the Act of Union, two other external partnerships appeared: in 1709 of one Captain Brodie, 'indweller in Edinburgh' and two partners surnamed Grant; and the other in 1710 of John Gage, merchant in Banff, and Donald Tayliour, merchant in London – further proof of the attraction of English capital to the deluded idea that there was money in Scots pine. The laird ultimately preferred the Banff-London partners to the Edinburgh-based ones. Gage was still busy five years later, when he gave a discharge to the laird for the work of no fewer than 300 men to clear rocks in the Bennie, a remarkable testimony to the number of men the laird of Rothiemurchus could apparently call together from his estates to perform direct labour.[4]

These engineering operations on the burns were no doubt related to the same partnership's contract with the Duke of Gordon to cut pine timber in Glenmore, for which permission ('a servitude') was needed for floating through Rothiemurchus ground. When the Banff-London partnership gave up, apparently frightened off by the 1715 rebellion, the Duke of Gordon was able to replace them for a decade in Glenmore by a new English partnership from Durham and Stockton, for whom he built a new sawmill on Rothiemurchus ground 'at the upper end of the waggon road'.[5] Correspondence of the same period, however, seems to imply that the Rothiemurchus estate had then taken the exploitation of their woods back into their own management.[6]

The next speculative adventure at Rothiemurchus was more ambitious than ever, and still more ill-fated. In 1738, James Grant, eldest son of the ageing

Patrick Grant, the sixth laird, encountered an Englishman named John Lummis, who is named in other documents as a 'wood surveyor' of Sheriff Hailes in Shropshire or of Preston in Lancashire. Lummis is implicated elsewhere in bargains that went badly wrong because the wood could not be extracted or because it did not live up to expectations. He enticed a company of Whitehaven men to buy pine from Donald Cameron of Lochiel in 1739, a venture which ended in the courts, and a partnership from Preston and Liverpool to buy pine from Roderick Chisholm of Strathglass in 1742, which also ended in futility and litigation. Lummis in addition had personal interests in woodland at Callart on Loch Leven that he wanted to sell for charcoal manufacture.[7]

In this case he persuaded James Grant to write him a letter after his visit to Rothiemurchus detailing the timber on the estates, 'as you have seen and experimented'. Grant claimed in the letter that the estate contained 20,000 acres covered with firwoods, that each acre contained nearly 50,000 trees, that therefore there were 100 million trees available (no one seems to have noticed that the sum should have amounted to a billion trees). All this was actually nonsense, as the best calculations that can be made from estate maps and other sources suggest that in the eighteenth century the woodland amounted to at most some 5000 or 6000 acres. It was also a mixed wood, not entirely pine. The botanist James Robertson emphasised that it was diverse, having 'abundance of excellent fir and birch, together with some hazle and poplar'.[8]

James Grant went on to say that the wood would be found to contain at least five million trees that would yield timber six inches square measured six feet above the ground, and that 300,000 of the largest would yield timber twelve inches square at that height: 'the least dimensions of the trees are sixty foot in height'. If the trees were felled over a period of 30 years, they would be worth £1,000 a year to the estate, but he was willing to let them go for a thirty year contract at a mere £500 a year. Would Mr Lummis please try to find some English merchant who would take them off his hands?[9]

It was a letter probably designed by Grant and Lummis in collaboration, and it worked. A Hull merchant partnership of Andrew Perrott and David Field rose to the bait, though they were cautious enough to send their own 'servants' to view the wood on their behalf: these were later to claim that the Grant foresters took them 'twice or thrice through the same places of purpose to make them believe there was a great abundance of trees in the wood', a statement which the Grants naturally indignantly denied. Nevertheless, at the time Perrott and Field were satisfied that 'the wood is as good as the best Norway wood', and agreed to buy and cut at a fixed rate 40,000 trees anywhere in the wood, half of them to be 10-12 inches square: the bargain was later varied to allow the merchants to cut 40,000 trees of any size they chose.

Within two years, however, Perrott and Field gave up after paying Grant £400 for pines and some other sums: they had not been able to find 500 trees of the larger dimension in the whole wood, and claimed that there were not 2,000 in the wood even six inches square at ten feet above the ground. Altogether they had felled 9,000 trees in two years, and they were trying to escape from a contract that was less profitable than they had hoped, for reasons that had nothing to do with conditions at Rothiemurchus. No doubt the truth lay between the two extremes so dramatically portrayed by their lawyers' pleadings, but even before legal proceedings commenced the merchants had privately written to the laird to say that the wood was too young and too small to cut with profit. That the laird was not on the strongest ground is also indicated by his immediate offer in court to settle for a payment of £1,000 instead of the £4,000 he had originally claimed.[10]

This was the last time that the Grants of Rothiemurchus invited outsiders to exploit their woods, but their experience at this point was not very different from the owners of Abernethy, Grant of Grant, or the owners of Glenmore, the Duke of Gordon or, for that matter, from owners of pine woods in the north and west like the Chisholms in Strathglass or the Camerons of Lochiel. It was summarised in 1781 by legal presentation in a dispute with the Duke of Gordon about rights to float wood through the Rothiemurchus estate down to the Spey:

> A number of English adventurers since the Union have been allured from the prospect of manufacturing wood that paid no [import] duty, and relying probably on the unfavourable opinion that had been conceived in England of the want of industry in the inhabitants of the Highlands of Scotland and a total ignorance of the use of any sort of machinery or management of water carriage, have induced attempts from time to time to manufacture Highland woods to be sent to England to be consumed there; though, so far as the memorialist can learn, few if any of these adventurers have had cause to boast of the profits they have just acquired.[11]

The rather superior tone of the Rothiemurchus lawyers at this juncture conceals the fact that the Grants themselves had again recently dabbled in the English market and burned their fingers, but this time more personally. William, brother to Patrick the eighth laird, had followed a prosperous medical career in London, and in his sojourn in the capital became convinced of the commercial possibilities of selling hollowed pine logs to the London water companies, in competition with the English elm that they usually used. In 1770 he persuaded his reluctant brother to allow the operation of a boring mill on the estate and the despatch of an experimental cargo of logs, bored and unbored, via Garmouth.

William was full of energy and optimism about the venture, his brother always less so. After a year the doctor made arrangements to operate alone, and for four years cut, bored and shipped timber to London on his own account: he provided about 4,000 pipes in all, 'good, bad and indifferent'. In the end the price of elm fell so low that Rothiemurchus wood became uncompetitive, and in 1774 the venture was abandoned.[12]

The small size of the trees, however, had, just as with Perrott and Field, been a continuous handicap to the boring mill. William Grant had difficulty in supplying the optimal size, trees of ten inches in diameter, from which pipes could be made of three or four inches diameter. Taken in conjunction with the complaints of the Hull merchants, it seems that few of the Rothiemurchus trees were of the dimensions that Steven and Carlisle tell us is normal in twentieth-century Scottish pine woods, usually between five and six feet circumference at breast height.[13]

If they were so small, what was the reason? It seems unlikely that the English adventurers from 1658 were able to despoil them so thoroughly, as their operations were so intermittent and unsuccessful. Much more likely as an explanation is the activities of local people, cutting frequently wood of modest size that would be convenient for simple tools and carriage by horseback, and which would mainly be used for building small houses. The Rothiemurchus estate accounts are not complete enough to give a full picture of this activity, but we know, for example, that in 1766 there were 106 buyers of wood 'at the back of Lochinnellan', all local men apart from one from Cromarty. Between 1769 and 1771 two-thirds of the wood sales was in 'sparwood', totalling 13,823 pieces: most of the rest was in deal plank, 'milnsawn deals' predominating over 'handsawn deals', but only the former going to Garmouth, the only sales outwith the local area. On average, wood sales of this sort realised £370 per annum, more than twice the rental of the farms of Rothiemurchus and nearly twice as much per year as the total of £400 that Perrott and Field actually paid for their two years' operations in 1739 and 1740.[14] One can understand the reluctance of the laird to support his brother's boring mill if that speculation was to interfere with his steady income from country trade.

Shortly after the collapse of William Grant's pipe mill, however, the estate became embroiled in a long dispute with the Duke of Gordon over the right to float timber down the Spey: they were partners in the case with other proprietors on Speyside, but especially Sir James Grant of Grant, who owned Abernethy. The laird of Rothiemurchus claimed to be selling £1,500 worth of wood a year, to go down river: the claim was ridiculed as a 'pompous sum', perhaps a slip of translating Scots money as sterling (i.e. only worth one twelfth of the claim!).[15] Indeed, surviving records make it hard to see that the wood was ever worth more than a few hundred a year, probably less than £500. It is true that Alexander Wight was told in the early 1780s that 'the wood is let to undertakers who pay about £1,200 sterling yearly', but he was probably only repeating what Patrick Grant told him, to reinforce his claim in the courts.[16]

The outcome of this dispute probably damaged the timber trade of the Rothiemurchus estate by making it illegal to float between 15 May and 26 August, which made it difficult to catch the most profitable market. Certainly according to estate accounts the trade was only worth £256 by 1786-7.[17] By then the rental of the farms had climbed to £420, and in 1787 Patrick Grant drew up an unusual deed of entail intended to halt the exploitation of woods for a generation. It would not be lawful for his heirs 'to fell, cut, sell or dispose of any of the fir woods' for 20 years, 'except the misgrown woods called garrocks, and decayed wood, or wood that shall fall or be thrown over or damaged by wind, storm or other accident'. At the conclusion of the period, the woods could be sold but the money raised from the sale, up to a total of £40,000, had to be placed in a fund to buy land as contiguous to the present estate as possible.[18] The entire land of the estate was also entailed at the same time.

Patrick's motives must have been mixed. No doubt he mistrusted the wisdom and frugality of the young heir. No doubt he was exhausted by litigation with his neighbour, with whom he had had another expensive dispute about rights to float wood down the Bennie in 1780. Probably he considered that the woods needed resting, and would be more valuable if they were allowed to grow larger timber: Perrott and Field had told the estate as much as long ago as 1740. Probably he noted the changing ratio of the value of his woods and his farms, and considered it a good strategy to use the former in due course to buy more of the latter. Finally, he was in debt himself by the time of his death.

The entail did not immediately end the sale of wood. There is an account of deals, spars and oars sold to fourteen people at Rothiemurchus in 1795, worth £293. It is hard to believe it was fully legal, and that all the wood came from garrocks or windthrow as allowed by entail. But there were no further sales recorded in the later extant rentals of 1802, and of 1806-7.[19]

There are few detailed indications of eighteenth-century woodland management. We know that the woods were unfenced, that the Grants appointed foresters who were probably tenants given a general responsibility of care for the wood, that from time to time the Baron Court met and punished general offences within the forest, such as poaching roe deer and cutting wood for local use without permission, or taking 'candle fir' from the trees.[20] It seems likely, from estate maps, that the general extent of the woodland was comparable to its extent today.[21] It also seems probable that the method of exploitation was to fell trees before they became inconveniently large, and to do so selectively rather than to clear fell. That does not rule out the reservation of some big trees that might have been grown on for particular purposes. Certainly the house of the old Doune contained pine baulks 16 feet by 12 inches by 3 inches and the new Doune, built towards 1800, baulks 17 feet long and a foot square. They must, in their day, have come from large fine trees.[22] But these, it appears, were the exception, at least by the eighteenth century.

The Nineteenth Century, 1800–1827

The exploitation of the Rothiemurchus woods in the first part of the nineteenth century was far more intensive than at any previous period, partly because it was driven by a greater economic need and partly because there was more opportunity. John Peter Grant, the ninth laird was, as we have seen (chapter 2 above), consumed by a fatal ambition to succeed on a wider stage, but handicapped by a constitutional inability to live within his means – even though these had been, initially, substantial.

By 1807, he was feeling the pinch, just as his political career got into its stride. It was the year in which he narrowly failed to take the Parliamentary seat of Morayshire despite having spent, according to his daughter, up to £20,000 on canvassing: by standing against the second son of his Chief, he had alienated the Grants of Grant into the bargain.[23] It was also the year when he over-invested in improvements to the Hertfordshire estate of Twyford which he had inherited from a relative, and sold it after a disastrous speculation in cattle. Thirdly, it was the year when the twenty-year moratorium on the felling of the Rothiemurchus woods ended: he could now fell them if he could get £10,000 for the first sale, but under the entail all the money for the foreseeable future would have to be put to the purchase of nearby farms. Such conditions did not suit John Peter at all. In 1808 he obtained a private act of Parliament that enabled him to vary the entail on the woods. In essence, he was allowed to buy from the estate for £10,000 most of the woods, to apply some of the money to liquidating debts left by the previous laird and with the remainder (£5042 6s. 4d.) either to invest in land or heritable securities that would become part of the entailed property, or to provide security for doing so. This complicated arrangement released capital immediately, particularly as John Peter chose not to pay out the sum, and the security he gave for doing so (the estate of Kinloss which he had bought from part of the proceeds of the sale of Twyford) ultimately turned out to be inadequate. In effect, from 1809, he was free either to sell the timber or to use it as security for more borrowing, or both. One small section, round Loch-an-Eilein, Loch Gamhna and the Lochans was reserved and remained legally protected from sale because the family considered it an essential part of the 'pleasure grounds of the manour of the Doune'.[24]

The economic climate was also exceptionally suitable for a more intensive exploitation of the pine woods. The Napoleonic Wars had cut off Britain from easy communication from Norway and the Baltic, whence came most of the softwood used in the towns and industrial areas, and after 1815, when peace returned, relatively heavy import duties were placed on foreign wood in an attempt to stimulate the Canadian timber trade by imperial preference. This had the incidental effect, at least for a time, of also maintaining the wartime profit margins for home grown Scottish wood.

Elizabeth Grant has left a famous account of the activity at Rothiemurchus in 1813, as the estate took charge of the operations of felling, floating, sawing and rafting, and began to replace the old single sawmills situated on the banks of the burns with a larger one near the Spey, holding double saws and concentrating labour.[25] Investment was increased in sluices and embankments. As early as the 1770s Patrick Grant had put sluices on the lochs to enable timber to be flushed down the streams, to the approbation of his brother William – 'I like vastly the idea of making sluices on all the lakes: that has something noble as well as useful in it'. By 1813 this system had been extended as far up as Loch Einich, and Elizabeth Grant describes a fatal accident in this 'very high and stormy glen' when the young keeper of the sluice gates went to open them in a winter storm.[26]

As the years passed, the affairs of John Peter became more and more tortuous, and the need to keep up the flow of wood more compelling. In 1811 the woods had been conveyed as security to a trust of creditors, consisting of a cousin, James Grant of Burnhall, WS and banker, and two or three others, for 40 years or until the debts had been liquidated. They had the right to fell trees above nineteen inches in circumference at five feet from the ground. The income of the wood was to service the debts, and John Peter remained in charge. In 1817 the trust apparently consented to the consignment of £6500 worth of wood to John Baxter, surgeon in Edinburgh, 'after making allowance and deductions of all fair and necessary expenses' for its manufacture and floating to Garmouth, apparently as security for a further loan. He probably received it, as he does not appear among future creditors. That the woods could have yielded such a sum would have seemed incredible to his father and uncle back in the 1770s, but, as we shall see, it was apparently not exceptional for the period.[27]

In 1820, an alteration in the trust arrangement placed William Patrick, heir to John Peter and then aged 22, in charge of the practical arrangements for managing the wood. Elizabeth remarked with a customary touch of acerbity that 'my father was to proceed as usual: London and the House in spring, and such improvements as amused him when at home'.

According to his sister, William Patrick successfully revolutionised the exploitation of the woods. He brought to an end 'the general felling of timber at whatever spot the men so employed found it most convenient to them to put an axe to a marked tree', and he introduced instead a system of rotational clear-fell:

> William made a plan of the forest, divided it into sections, and as far as was practicable allotted one portion to be cleared immediately, enclosed by a stout fencing, and then left to nature, not to be touched again for fifty or sixty years. The ground was so rich in seed that no other course was necessary. By the following spring a carpet of inch-high plants would be struggling to rise above the heather, in a season or two more a thicket of young firs would be found there, thinning themselves as they grew, the larger destroying all the weaker. Had this plan been pursued from the beginning there would never have been an end to the wood of Rothiemurchus.[28]

He next centralised the provision of horses to work in the wood from the Doune itself, employing them out of season in carting deals to Forres and bringing back meal, or in carrying coal from Inverness: on the estate 'the little bodies and idle boys with ponies were got rid of'. In a similar way the operations of the lesser mills were concentrated on one large building at Inverdruie, equipped with 'a coarse upright saw for slabbing', several 'packs of saws which cut the whole log up at once into deals'. A smaller compartment of the large mill was fitted up with circular saws for the purpose of preparing the thinnings of the birch woods for herring-barrel staves – 'it was a mere toy beside its gigantic neighbour, but a very pretty and a very profitable one, above £1,000 a year being cleared by this manufacture of what had hitherto been valueless except as fuel'.[29]

William Patrick also gave an independent account of how he had managed the forest in a report to the creditors in 1824, and, though not being so precise about the division into sections, confirmed much of what Elizabeth recollected.

He explained that before he took over, the workforce lived and laboured all over the forest and took whatever they found most convenient for cutting, virtually unsupervised, 'the forest was picked according to their fancy'. Consequently much was left to rot in the woods, and was prepared so badly that great expense was incurred at Garmouth fitting it for the market. Nor could it be dragged to the water until the forester had come and accounted for it, and this meant long delays while the timber deteriorated. Much was cut into deals, when floating logs would have been more profitable, and workers were paid in advance, with meal, for work that they sometimes failed to undertake.

He explained that when he took over in 1820 his first action was to clear the forest of all the scattered, cut wood that was preventing regeneration all over the forest – 'there was hardly a spot where the axe had not been at work', and all the profits of the following year were consumed in this tidying operation. He then centralised cutting in one place at a time, under the eye of a foreman, who prepared each tree according to its qualities. Similarly he abolished the old mills dispersed through the forest, and sent much down the Spey in log (a quirk of the import duties made it more profitable to do it this way) but still manufacturing at one big mill at Inverdruie 'the whole trimmings of the timber and all the small rubbish in the forest'. Workers were paid weekly by the foreman, in money or meal, on piece rates for work actually performed. Less reliance was placed on the horses of the small tenants, and more on the more powerful animals kept at the Doune, partly because in late springs like that of 1823 the tenants needed their animals to cultivate the land at exactly the time when it was necessary to get the wood to the Spey to beat the floating moratorium of 15 May.[30]

The occasion for the report of 1824 was mounting discontent among the creditors. James Grant of Burnhall, clearly pressed by his own financial problems, accused John Peter Grant of earning £15,000–£20,000 from the woods and applying it to service new debts rather than to paying old ones. John Peter managed to convince the trust that this was not the case. He admitted to having sold £9,000 worth of wood at Garmouth in the year from 1 September 1822, but explained that 40% of that sum was swallowed up by the expenses of manufacturing the timber and floating it to Garmouth. The remainder had been paid to the trust, as testified by the accounts. James Grant apologised, but the administration of the trust passed to a new man, Patrick Borthwick, whose Leith merchant partnership had contracted to sell the timber at Garmouth on terms apparently less expensive to the trustees. Nevertheless it is clear from this point that they were more suspicious of John Peter, and more doubtful that they would ever see their money back, than ever before: a reconstituted trust, headed by Borthwick, secured powers to sequester his personal moveable effects including the plate, library and furniture at the Doune, and all unentailed assets on the estate, should it become necessary to limit their own losses. Meanwhile William Patrick remained in charge of the wood. The total debts due to the trustees in 1824 were said to amount to about £65,000.[31]

All this raises the question of what the forest was actually worth, and what was sold from it at this period. Papers relating to the affairs of James Grant in 1829 speak of the wood having been valued at 'between £60,000 and £90,000 a few years ago' and state that 'these woods have produced about £10,000 per annum' in the past, but 'owing to the depression of the times for some years back, the sales of that wood have been very limited and little of the debt has been paid'.[32] Sir Thomas Dick Lauder in 1834 maintained that it had once yielded large profits over many years, sometimes over £20,000 a year, but he was less likely to be well informed than James Grant and his lawyers.[33] There are no extant estate accounts to guide us, only occasional statements like the apparently reliable figure of £9,000 gross yield for the wood in 1822-3 – not a year likely to have been particularly outstanding.

The figure of £10,000 mentioned by James Grant's lawyers was presumably intended to be net – i.e. the profit available to the trust after the cost of manufacturing in the woods and floating to Garmouth had been taken into account. John Peter Grant put the cost at 40%, roughly equally divided between manufacturing and floating, and his figure was not challenged. Later estimates put the figure at 25% or 30%, but in 1831 they appear to have exceeded 50%.[34] At all events they appear to have been substantial. But whether the sums mentioned are net or gross, they are extremely substantial compared to eighteenth-century yields, even allowing for changes in the value of money, and also very much larger than anything obtained from the wood later.

It is also worth noticing that if £10,000 net really was obtained in one year from a wood only estimated at six to nine times that value, William Patrick's plan to cut on sustainable rotation would have been quickly overtaken by events – as proved to be the case. But the wood was all the creditors had by way of a regular income from the estate: the value of the farm rental by 1824 was apparently not in excess of £250 a year, or about one twentieth of the net yield from the wood. This was an extraordinary contrast with the eighteenth century: in 1769-71 the farms had yielded on average about half the net yield of the wood, and in 1786-7 when the rental of the farms considerably exceeded the net yield of the wood. In essence, if the creditors were ever to see their loans repaid, they had to get as much out of the wood as they could as quickly as they could.

In 1827, John Peter's financial house of cards finally collapsed. The trust sequestered the moveable assets of the estate, the diary of the mill at Inverdruie recorded supplying 21 deals 'for packing boxes for the Doune family'[35] and the family made a rapid exit to India. A few months before this dramatic *denouement*, the workers in the sawmill complained through their foreman of non-payment of wages. They were in turn upbraided by William Patrick for their disloyalty in making such a complaint, in an address which he had printed in Gaelic and English:

> I will never hear from any individual a particular complaint, without inquiring into it... but I tell you distinctly that I will not listen to any reports affecting you, that I hear from other people nor to any general complaint that you may think fit as a body to make.

Many of the workers, he went on, had worked on the estate for generations, or been for years in domestic service:

> Men who have imbibed an affectionate regard to our family almost with their mother's milk ...When such men go wrong...when any of them shew a temporary estrangement of their regard to their hereditary proprietors, I will confess that it gives me pain; but it is a pain of the nature of which a father feels at the misconduct of his children; it leads me rather to feel anxious to restore you to the right feeling you have departed from, than angrily to leave you to the mischievous effects of your own folly, and to cast you off forever.[36]

It was a virtuoso exercise, from one not yet thirty years old, in the art of blaming the victim.

The Nineteenth Century, 1827-1900

The departure of the family by no means brought the employment of the hapless workforce to an immediate end, as the trustees were more anxious than ever to get some of their money back, a situation complicated by the bankruptcy of James Grant of Burnhall two years later. Felling continued throughout the 1830s, though in 1831 the trustees reported on difficulties due to low prices brought about by competition from America and Norway, compounded for 'Rothiemurchus and other natural timber of Scotch growth' by the 'increasing use, in the north country, of planted fir timber which is now sold at a price which would yield to the creditors almost no return upon the Rothiemurchus timber, owing to the expence necessarily incurred in bringing it from the forest to the mouth of the Spey'.[37] That year the rental of Rothiemurchus (which would have included the rent of the Doune to the Duchess of Bedford) was £1,107, while the net yield on wood sales was £1,872 (£3,840 gross). Over the following three years sales remained at a similar level, averaging £1,600 net (£2,100 gross), the costs of manufacture and floating temporarily dropping as a proportion of the price, but the actual quantities of wood marketed also apparently falling as the forest became exhausted. In 1836, the creditors obtained permission to sell standing the remaining trees round the lochs, which had been originally reserved in the arrangements of 1809: they were sold for £2,500 but after deductions only realised £420. Finally, a document of 1839 revealed that over the previous five years the woods had yielded on average of £1,526 per annum (£2,875 gross), little enough compared to the past, but more than double the yield of the rents (including the Doune) in that year.[38]

By then, however, the forest had been largely, but not completely, clear felled. In 1834 Sir Thomas Dick Lauder described Rothiemurchus and Glenmore as 'now equally denuded of all their forest timber', but regenerating fast and in a way that was certain to produce valuable wood in due course:

> The young saplings come up as thick as they do in a nurseryman's seed bed, and in the same *relative* degree of thickness do they continue to grow, till they are old

enough to be cut down. The competition that takes place between the adjacent individual plants, creates a rivalry that increases their upward growth whilst the exclusion of the air prevents the formation of lateral branches or destroys them soon after they are formed. Thus Nature produces by far the most valuable timber, for it is tall, straight, of uniform diameter throughout its whole length, and free from knots... the large and spreading trees are on the outskirts of the masses.[39]

In 1839, John Grigor, the well-known nurseryman and seedsman of Forres, reported in similar terms that the old forest is 'much exhausted', but 'many beautiful clumps of pines still remain'. Like Dick Lauder, he was struck by their slender and tall quality – 'the trees almost stand of a uniform size, measuring at 6 feet high 4½ feet in circumference, and nearly of the same girth to the height of about 35 feet', going on to achieve an average height of about 70 feet. The stumps of felled trees of similar dimension were, from their rings, 120 to 125 years old, which would take their origin back to the decade after the Act of Union. He also noted that the marshy hollows within the forest, 'now too wet for pine', were crowded with the roots of smaller trees, that the close-growing trees on the knolls crowded out other vegetation, and that young natural pine was growing well.[40] These accounts may be compared with internal reports on the forest of 1831, which described the old reserved wood as containing 11,248 trees with an average of 12 to 13 cubic feet of timber per tree, valued other old timber available for felling at £6,267 gross, and also referred to the 'young wood of Rothiemurchus ... growing before 1808' as containing 23,500 trees over 30 years old (but none in this category over 50-60 years old). The wood was divided into lots, evidently reflecting William's reorganisation, but there is no sign that they were to be felled in rotation. Presumably by 1839 when Grigor wrote, little was left except in the category of the former reserved wood along with regrowth from recent felling.[41]

Finally, when Elizabeth Grant returned on a nostalgic visit to Rothiemurchus in 1846, she found the old sawmill all but deserted, took a walk 'through the young fir forest' and spoke of 'a young forest to replace the fallen': when two years later the Calcutta banking scandal engulfed William Patrick and the income of the estate was likely to be impounded by new creditors, she wrote bitterly of the sequestration of 'the few trees fit for the axe in that once fine forest', estimating their value at almost £9,000.[42]

This valuation may well have been roughly based on another detailed report on the forest, drawn up in April 1848 by Neil MacLean of Inverness. He calculated the number of the 'old reserved trees' – the survivors reserved from the sale of 1809 – at around 10,000 yielding on average about 15 cu.ft of timber per tree. He estimated the current price of pine timber at Garmouth at 1s. 2d. per foot, from which 30% had to be deducted for cutting, dragging and floating down the Spey, and recommended that a third of the trees be taken out now, as they were approaching maturity. These, he thought, would realise £2,000, so the value of the whole stand was presumably £6,000. The value of the rest of forest he could not accurately state, but pointed out that there could be a potential market for thinnings from the regenerating forest, though given the current price of wood this would probably not repay the effort. He commented on the 'general spread of natural fir seedlings in this locality' as 'most remarkable', and said it seemed only necessary to enclose a piece of ground in the forest 'to give rise at once to a thick and healthy crop of young trees'. On these grounds he predicted that in 50 or 60 years time the forest would be of far greater value than ever it had been in the past. Already, interestingly, what we now call 'granny pines' were seen as worth preserving for aesthetic reasons: 'such of the old branchy trees as are more picturesque than useful for timber will not I suppose be touched under any circumstances.'[43]

At that time William Patrick had once more been managing Rothiemurchus for six years, albeit by correspondence from India, following re-negotiation with new trustees headed by his sister Jane's father-in-law in 1842 (see chapter 2). William Patrick's management apparently continued for a time when he returned disgraced from India in 1848, only for him to lose control in 1855 and to resume it again by the 1860s. Nevertheless, it is safe to say that all the major investment decisions on the estate for three decades after 1842 were his and, as we have seen in chapter 2, he proved a vigorous and proactive land manager.

His approach to the forest was summed up in his own words as 'to attend to systemateck method of turning the prime timber into money, and of keeping up a continual succession of such prime timber' – no different, in fact, from his aims in 1820. However, in 1842:

> When I acquired dominion over Rothiemurchus so much of the prime timber had been felled and so little regard paid to the reproduction of it that I determined to put a stop for a time to the manufacture and to give all my care to growing material.[44]

He set about this by renewed planting and enclosing. Some planting had taken place before, as there are references to planting and also to larch as early as 1824. When Lord Cockburn visited Aviemore in April, 1839 and fantasised about the house and woods he would like to create on 'one of the grandest inland places in Scotland', he said:

> We must begin by clearing the country of at least nineteen parts out of every twenty of that abominable larch with which it pleased the late Rothiemurchus, as it still pleases many Highland lairds, to stiffen and blacken the land.'[45]

William may well have been responsible for those plantings, and in 1842 he had a plan drawn up for planting Cambusmore, which was probably at least partly carried out while his brother was in temporary residence at the Doune. In the winter of 1846-7 he had, by correspondence from Calcutta, planted almost half a million trees, of which 433,000 were larch and 39,000 Weymouth pine, and the remainder a blend of hardwoods: 2,000 oaks, about 1,000 each of Norway maple, 'tan willows' and beech and a thousand assorted elms, 'planes or limes', rowans, Italian black poplars and Italian white poplars, as well as 6,000 hawthorns for hedges.[46]

Simultaneously, he started 'removing obstructions to the natural growth of trees for which the place is wonderfully adapted', by securing the forest from 'the depradations of domestick beasts pasturing among young trees'. Again, this was not totally novel, as before 1824 'a large flock of sheep' kept on the farm had been 'dismissed, for the preservation of the woods'. Now, however, he entirely abandoned all hill or unenclosed pasture on the estate and enclosed all the lower or farm lands with three stone dykes, two along the estate marches running up from the Spey to points above the cultivated land, where they intersected with a 'Forest Dyke' that kept the farms and the natural wood apart. All but 900 yards of this had been completed when work was temporarily ended because of the new bankruptcy. William Patrick was exceedingly proud of this achievement, though Elizabeth slightingly referred to it as 'that absurd wall of such enormous extent over the mountains and round the woods of Rothiemurchus'.[47] He protected his new plantations by temporary fencing to keep out red deer and roe deer 'which have free scope in the forest', but at this point they were probably at low density. The early decision to keep the hill ground free of sheep probably accounts for the fact that Rothiemurchus is apparently unique in Great Britain as a place where a natural tree line can still be seen.

There is little information about the forest in the 1850s, but average wood sales over the years 1851-3 reached only £214, compared to an enhanced estate rental of £1,134. From the early 1860s, William was busy again with planting, not discouraged by a letter from his agent in 1856 which mentioned that, although natural regeneration was doing well, the previous attempts at planting had 'in a great measure failed, particularly the hard woods'.[48] In 1861, he planted (or replanted) about 3,000 hardwoods around the Doune. In 1862 he noted: 'this season I planted the Moor of Callert in I believe the third time. My brother John planted it with larch in one of the early 1840s. When I saw it the appearance was wretched and would have been better without a plant'. He decided, since Scots pine was regenerating on the western part of the moor, to plant more pine among the surviving larches and to fence with tarred pine posts and wire.[49]

The following year he planted the eastern shore of Loch-an-Eilein, near to a thriving larch plantation, with a mixture of larch, Scots pine and Corsican pine. Scots pine was already regenerating there, but the ground was 'mostly full of strong heather ... there are frequent patches without any plants at all – I intend to plant the whole thing up to about four feet apart'. He had great faith in Corsican pine ('Laricco') as an infill for sparse Scots pine, believing it to be second only to larch and quicker in its growth than Scots pine. He bought 100,000 two-year old seedlings of Corsican pine in 1863, but there is only a little trace of it on the estate now.[50]

At that period he was planning timber sales to the railway companies 'as our principal market', arguing that iron and stone sleepers had both been tried and found wanting, and that one-sixth of creosoted timber sleepers needed to be replaced yearly, thus creating a constant market. He believed that a well-grown pine would provide four sleepers and a wooden block. Over 1864-5 the estate did indeed sell 16,727 sleepers to the railway, newly arrived in Strathspey and pushing ahead to Inverness.

Timber sales in the 1860s were stimulated by the railway in other ways, because it freed the business from expensive and inconvenient floating down the Spey to Garmouth. Anything loaded on a train waggon could go north and south to its market within hours. In 1863 some 30,000 trees were sold to a Forres merchant as sparwood for £2,625 – they were perhaps thinnings. The sale of the sleepers realised £2,369, and in the same year £500 worth of wood went to Garmouth. In the period 1862-4, £4,982 worth of wood, some of it larch, and including 60,000 pit props, was sold from Loch-an-Eilein, Achnahatrick and Guislich, to a wood merchant at Crieff.[51]

All these bargains added up to about £2,600 a year, perhaps modest compared to the exploitation earlier in the century, but still enough to strain the productive capacity of the forest. By 1869 the heirs made it a condition of agreeing to a variation in part of the entail that, 'Mr. [William] Grant shall engage to cut no more wood. All the wood that is of an age to be fit for cutting I understand has been cut and none remains that could be cut in Mr. Grant's lifetime without grave waste'.[52] The woods seem to have been virtually clear-felled once more.

How good a steward of the wood was William Patrick? There is no sign that he ever tried to revive after 1842 the scheme which he devised as a young man in 1820 for dividing the wood into portions to be cut in rotation. Such a scheme is inherently more difficult in pinewoods than in oakwoods because of the unpredictable densities of regeneration.[53] Nor is there (we may think fortunately) any indication that his schemes for planting non-native softwoods met with much success, though some of the larch may have done so and been felled subsequently. Large individual larches can still be seen in the forest. His main contribution to the survival of the native forest was to build the enclosure dyke and abolish cattle and sheep grazing in the wood. He continued to be strict in keeping stock out, as a tenant farmer found to his cost in 1866, when a flock of sheep broke into a plantation of larch and Corsican pine at Cambusmore.[54]

At least, as his brother and successor put it in 1883, 'because sheep were abolished for the sake of the wood before deer were introduced', the estate was given a clean bill of health before the Napier Commission: no one appeared before the Commissioners at their meeting at Kingussie, and their secretary wrote to the laird that 'I suppose we may conclude there are no dissatisfied tenants on this estate'.[55]

That is not to say that there had not been economic hardships. In 1824 John Peter had reported to the trustees that total employment from the woods included a professional forester, a foreman at the sawmill, a superintendent acting as grieve, a meal store-keeper, a clerk who kept the books, between 36 and 40 woodmen (of whom 20 were at work at any one time when the season allowed) and 10 mill hands, apart from small tenants employed casually to draw the wood.[56] Elizabeth Grant on her return in 1846 found at the mill only three men and a boy, in place of 'a mob of workmen', hauliers and floaters as well as sawyers: 'the forest being gone no mill work is ever done beyond what is required for fencing'. She was taken aback by the social condition of the people, no better, she thought, in the last 20 years and 'far behind our Irish, not within half a century so much up to the times.[57]

But this was at the start, not at the conclusion, of William Patrick's main period of management. Some at least of the employment returned, at least intermittently. In October and November 1862 he was employing 30 workmen, eighteen regularly, on extracting 'lime and sleepers'.[58]

Little more active management seems to have taken place in the forest before the end of the century. On William's death in 1874 they were surveyed again in great detail, in a report running to 43 pages. The net worth of the woods that could then be cut was only £2,341, and many of them were described as neglected. The report recommended little more than thinning and care; trees north of the old boring mill were described as 'a fine specimen of the old wood and might be kept for particular estate purposes', and those at the west end of Loch-an-Eilein comprised 'a number of full grown trees of the old forest still left which might be cleared away with advantage as they will never be of more value than at present and many of them are doing damage to the young wood'. These were presumably the last of the eighteenth-century growth.[59] So little wood was left that when in 1877 the Doune was rebuilt it was panelled in Canadian pine delivered by railway to Aviemore.[60]

A separate report of 1874 concerned William's dyke separating the forest from the farmland. It was described as 6,415 yards long, stone built with earth backing, 4½ feet high with a row of 6 inch turf sods on top, and surmounted by a slight wooden paling supported by posts driven into the dyke: except for its great length (over three and a half miles) it was a typical woodland enclosure of its time. The surveyor described it as now decayed and no longer a proper fence for keeping the deer in or the sheep out. He recommended repair, and replacement of the turf and wooden topping by wire. It is this reconstructed dyke that the visitor sees in places along the edge of the forest today.[61]

In the final quarter of the nineteenth century the primary use of the forest was as part of a sporting estate: in 1892-3, for example, the rental from the shootings was £1,585, from the farms £1,300 and there was no mention of any income from the wood. Indeed, at this stage the wood could never have produced, in a sustained way, any income to equal that from sporting rents. In 1896 the game bag for the year amounted to 92 stags (average weight of 70 was 14 stone), 54 hinds, 14 roe, 108 brace of red grouse and 8 brace of black grouse.[62] Presumably there had always been a few deer in the woods, but they were certainly reinforced by introductions from elsewhere some time before 1883.

Nevertheless, by the end of the century, felling had begun again. In 1899-1900, the woods yielded £501 for small quantities sold to a buyer in Pitlochry, compared to income from rents and farms amounting to £3,564: the yield of the wood increased to £2,197 in 1900-1901 (to buyers in Pitlochry and Aberdeen) and stood at £1,557 in 1901-2, again to Pitlochry.[63] Sending wood south had become much easier since the advent of the railway in the 1860s, but it was only intermittently worthwhile to do so.

We have not attempted to trace the history of the wood in the twentieth century. It was marked by heavy felling episodes in both world wars carried out on government instructions by Canadian and Indian workers, but otherwise by low levels of extraction. Clearly there was also a disinclination by the lairds to make the land available for Forestry Commission or other commercial planting. W H Murray in 1962 mentioned a 'recent' proposal by the Forestry Commission to 'fell the old Caledonian pines of Rothiemurchus', which had been modified 'only at the intervention of the Prime Minister, acting on appeal by the member of Parliament for Inverness-shire and by Colonel J P Grant'.[64] The nature of this incident remains obscure, but the Forestry Commission was involved in compulsory purchase proposals in other places in the 1950s. In 1954, the declaration of a National Nature Reserve in the Cairngorms, and subsequent nature reserve agreements signed between the estate and the Nature Conservancy and its successor bodies, strengthened the protection of the ancient wood, which is now valued as a prime site of surviving Caledonian pine forest and guarded by European as well as by British legislation.

No one, however, can read its history and remain under the beguiling illusion that it is the untouched wilderness that it can seem to the visitor on a quiet summer day. Rather, it is the outstanding example of a pine forest's ability to recover from heavy economic use, providing the ecological processes that enable it to do so remain intact. The Rothiemurchus woods are there because they were permitted to regenerate, but not because they were spared the woodman's axe.

Notes

1   Arthur Mitchell (ed.), *Geographical Collections relating to Scotland made by Walter Macfarlane*, three volumes, Edinburgh: Scottish History Society, 1906, III, 240-242.

2   Doune papers, 48: J. Munro, 'The Golden Groves of Abernethy: the cutting the extraction of timber before the Union', in G. Cruickshank (ed.), *A Sense of Place: Studies in Scottish Local History* (Scotland's Cultural Heritage, Edinburgh, 1988), pp.160-1.

3   I am indebted to Dr. Pat Dennison for this information.

4   Doune papers, 82, 83: and correspondence of 1715. It is, however, possible that 300 man-days is implied rather than the labour of 300 individual people.

5   SRO: GD 44/29/6/24 and 2/10.

6   See Doune papers, correspondence, especially a letter of William Stewart, Garmouth, 1720.

7   For Lummis, see NLS: Haldane papers, letters from Donald Cameron dated 2 July 1739 and 21 April 1740 (I am indebted to Professor Allan Macinnes for these references); SRO: RD 2/151, 21 April 1742; J. Munro (ed.), *The Inventory of Chisholm Writs, 1456-1810* (Scottish Record Society, n.s. 18, Edinburgh, 1884), p.167.

8   D.M. Henderson and J.H. Dickson (eds.), *A Naturalist in the Highlands: James*

Robertson, His Life and Travels in Scotland, 1767-1771 (Edinburgh, 1994), p.167.

9   Doune papers: 600.

10   *Ibid.*

11   Doune papers: 343.

12   Doune papers: correspondence of 1770-1774.

13   H.M. Steven and A. Carlisle, *The Native Pinewoods of Scotland* (Oliver and Boyd, Edinburgh, 1959), p.77.

14   Doune papers: 143.

15   Doune papers: *Memorial for Sir James Grant, etc., and Memorial for Alexander, Duke of Gordon, etc.*, both Edinburgh, 1780.

16   Alexander Wight, *Present State of Husbandry in Scotland* (Edinburgh, 1778-1784), Vol. IV, p.210.

17   Doune papers: 190.

18   Doune papers: *Memorial and queries for John Peter Grant, Esquire, of Rothiemurchus for the Opinion of Counsel, 1808*, pp.1-2.

19   Doune papers: 224, 310.

20   Doune papers: 149.

21   Doune papers: 'Plan of the Mains of the Down of Rothiemurchus surveyed by William Henderson, 1762' and 'Plan of the estate of Rothiemurchus, surveyed by Archibald Tait, 1789'.

22   David Warren, *pers. comm.* Mr. Warren worked on the recent restoration of the Doune.

23   Elizabeth Grant, *Memoirs of a Highland Lady* (ed. A. Tod, Edinburgh, 1988), pp.71-3.

24   Doune papers: *An Act for enabling the heirs of entail in possession for the time being of the lands and estate of Rothiemurchus ... to contract for the sale of the fir woods, 1808*: see also 211. The purchase sum was originally £11,500 but was reduced on the exclusion of the woods round the lochs.

25   Elizabeth Grant, *Highland Lady*, pp.268-275.

26   Doune papers: Correspondence 1770; *Statement of J.P. Grant of Rothiemurchus, 1824*; Elizabeth Grant, *Highland Lady*, p.275.

27   SRO: CS 96/2617, p.20; Doune papers: 470. It is possible that the 1817 transaction was not approved, as the contract at the Doune is an unsigned draft.

28   Elizabeth Grant, *Highland Lady*: pp.155-7.

29   *Ibid.*, pp.157-8.

30   Doune papers: Statement of J.P. Grant Esq., of Rothiemurchus and proposal for the liquidation of his debts, 1824.

31   Doune papers: *Statement of J.P. Grant ...*; "Trust disposition and assignation, J.P. Grant to Patrick Borthwick 9 June, 1824".

32   SRO: CS 96/2617, p.26.

33   See his edition of W. Gilpin, *Remarks on Forest Scenery and other Woodland Views* (Edinburgh, 1834), Vol. 2, p.175.

34   Doune papers: 315, 392.

35   Doune papers: uncatalogued diary of the sawmill.

36   Doune papers: 369, *W.P. Grant's address to the forest workmen and sawmillers, 1827.*

37   Doune papers: 319.

38   Doune papers: 315, 319, 356, 365, 481. The 'reserved' woods were bought by a

trustee on behalf of Sir John Peter Grant himself, and the sum of £420 was not distributed to the trustees but added to the entailed sum of £5042. 6s. 4d. Presumably the trustees found that, legally, they could not touch this residue: on the other hand some of the £2189 'deductions' may have gone into their pockets. I have not been able to unravel this transaction properly.

39   T. Dick Lauder in Gilpin, *Remarks on Forest Scenery*, Vol. 1, p.175.

40   J. Grigor, "Report on the native pine forests of Scotland", *Trans. of the Highland and Agricultural Society of Scotland*, 2nd ser., Vol. 6, pp.125-6. Steven and Carlisle, *Native Pinewoods*, p.122 seem to have misread Grigor: I can see no sign that he found regeneration 30 years old and 30 feet high.

41   Doune papers: 315, 392.

42   Elizabeth Grant, *The Highland Lady in Ireland: Journals, 1840—50*, (ed. P. Pelly and A. Tod, Edinburgh, 1991), pp.241-2, 402.

43   Doune papers: 392.

44   Doune papers: W.P. Grant's notebook.

45   H. Cockburn, *Circuit Journeys* (Edinburgh, 1888), pp.39-40.

46   Doune papers: 230; Plans of farms, 1819 (with additions).

47   Doune papers: W.P. Grant's notebook; *Statement of J.P. Grant, 1824*; Elizabeth Grant, *Highland Lady in Ireland*, p.417.

48   Doune papers: 319.

49   Doune papers: 479.

50   *Ibid.*

51   Doune papers: 481.

52   Doune papers: 328.

53   For instance, see J.M. Lindsay, 'The use of woodland in Argyllshire and Perthshire between 1650 and 1850', unpublished Ph.D. thesis, University of Edinburgh 1975, pp.241, 284-5.

54   Doune papers: 392. 'Precognition in the matter of destruction of young trees'.

55   Doune papers: 534.

56   Doune papers: *Statement of J.P. Grant, 1824*.

57   Elizabeth Grant, *Highland Lady in Ireland*, pp.242—247.

58   Doune papers: 481.

59   Doune papers: 489.

60   David Warren, *pers. comm.*

61   Doune papers: 489.

62   Doune papers: 483.

63   Doune papers: 335.

64   W.H. Murray, *Highland Landscape: a Survey* (National Trust for Scotland, Edinburgh, 1962), p.16.

Acknowledgement:

I am extremely grateful to John and Philippa Grant for unlimited access to the archives at the Doune, and much enjoyable hospitality.

7. Rothiemurchus: The Forest, its Ecology and Future Management

Philip R Ratcliffe

Introduction

Rothiemurchus is one of the largest and most important remnants of the once extensive natural forests of Scotland. Although pinewoods are the predominant woodland type at Rothiemurchus, it is important to perceive this within the wider context of a mosaic of interacting ecosystems incorporating riversides and riparian areas, bogs, muskeg and the natural forest tree-line. Birch and juniper are important constituents of the pinewoods and oak, willow and alder form separate associations in places. The forest supports relatively high levels of biodiversity, but this can almost certainly be improved upon.

Caledonian pinewoods are included as a priority habitat in the EC Habitats Directive. Thirty-three native pinewoods in Scotland are designated as Sites of Special Scientific Interest (SSSI) under the Wildlife and Countryside Act of 1981. A number of these have been proposed as Special Areas of Conservation (SACs) under the Habitats Directive, and are expected to become part of the 'Natura 2000' network of sites. Within the UK Biodiversity Action Plan, Native Pine Woodlands are targeted as an important ecosystem and a costed Habitat Action Plan (HAP) has been drafted.

An important objective of the Native Pine Woodland HAP is to restore and expand the natural diversity of composition and structure of the woodlands, and on a local scale at Rothiemurchus, a Woodland Biodiversity Action Plan is being prepared. An important underlying principle is that the future vision for the forest – the Desired Future Condition (DFC) – is not constrained by visions of some past natural state which might have occurred at some particular point in history, such as the immediate post-glacial, neolithic or mediaeval periods. Instead the DFC should be developed based on the prehistoric and historic evidence, on recent experience, and on future expectations, which will guarantee the sustainable delivery of a wide range of outputs in the future.

Building on the requirements of a range of sensitive, rare and threatened species which occur at Rothiemurchus, a vision of the future forest which caters for the need of all these species is developed. It is suggested that by providing a range of ecosystem components (or biodiversity surrogates) such as dead and decaying wood, which mimic the structure of natural forests, many species currently unknown at Rothiemurchus will be maintained. A pattern of woodlands, including some large patches, which are linked together to form a network can provide habitats of a size and contiguity which will support a wide range of species, while safeguarding the requirements of non-woodland species and land-uses.

Rothiemurchus in an international context

The Rio Conference

The United Nations Conference on Environment and Development (UNCED), held in Rio de Janeiro in 1992, established a major global impetus to ensure a sustainable future for the planet. The sustainable use of the world's biodiversity was a major part of the convention. UNCED led to a number of initiatives in Europe and in the UK which were designed to deliver the commitments made in Rio, including the sustainable management of forestry and the maintenance of biodiversity. Ratcliffe (1997) provides further details of these and the way in which they might influence local actions to increase forest biodiversity.

The Habitats Directive

The Habitats Directive is European law which provides for the creation of a network of protected areas across the European Union known as 'Natura 2000'. The main aims are to conserve the most important habitats and species in Europe and to promote the maintenance of biodiversity (Department of the Environment, 1995).

Caledonian Forest (native pine) is listed as a priority habitat in the Habitats Directive. This designation is based on the view that this habitat is in danger of disappearing in the European Community, and requires special and urgent protection measures to ensure its survival and subsequent enhancement.

The Helsinki Resolutions

The Ministerial Conference on the Protection of Forests in Europe at Helsinki in 1993 (Loiskekoski et al, 1993) established a basis for the sustainable management of European forests. The Helsinki conference established guidelines for the sustainable management and the conservation of biodiversity in European forests, recognising that the conservation of biodiversity is an essential component of sustainable management, and that it should be embodied in the preparation of forest policies, operational guidelines and legislation. The protection of primeval and special forests was emphasised.

Biodiversity: the UK Action Plan

Since 1992, the UK Biodiversity Action Plan (UKBAP) (Government Report, 1994a) has been progressed, and lists of target species and habitats have been drawn up, and Habitat Action Plans (HAPs) and Species Action Plans (SAPs) drafted for some of the most important ones (Government Report, 1995).

Native Pine Woodlands have been targeted as an important ecosystem, an

HAP has been drafted, and Species Action Plans (SAPs) have been drafted for some of the important pinewood species.

Sustainable Forestry: the UK Programme

This programme laid the foundations for the sustainable management of forests in the UK:

> The United Kingdom's forestry policy is based on the same fundamental tenet that forests and forest lands should be managed to meet the social, economic, ecological, cultural and spiritual human needs of present and future generations (Government Report, 1994b).

The Cairngorms

The forests of the Cairngorms are particularly significant, representing the most extensive example of boreal forest in Scotland. Much of the forest is relatively unmanaged, or it is managed on an extensive basis and contains high biological diversity. However, much of the forest is degraded in ecological terms and the continuity between different forest types, and between different structural types within forests, has to some extent been lost (Cairngorms Working Party, 1992). However, in a British context the woodland continuity and extent of large contiguous patches of forest is good.

Apart from Rothiemurchus, the woods of Strathspey and Deeside include other large and important pinewoods including those of Ballochbuie, Glen Tanar, Glen Quoich, Glen Lui, Glen Derry, Glen Feshie, Glen More and Abernethy. There are also a number of important native broadleaved woodland types which occur in the area.

The HAP for Native Pine Woodlands mainly addresses the expansion and restoration of natural diversity. It aims to restore the natural diversity of composition and structure of woodlands listed in the Caledonian Pinewood Inventory, regenerate and expand 35% of the current wooded area (16,046 ha) by the year 2005, create the conditions for the regeneration of a further 35% of the area over the next 20 years, and establish new native pine woods over a cumulative total of 25,000 ha by 2005 (equivalent to a further 155% of the existing remnant pine wood area).

The Cairngorms Partnership

In 1992 the Cairngorms Working Party (CWP) report to the Secretary of State for Scotland (Cairngorms Working Party 1992), recommended the development of an integrated management strategy for the Cairngorms. This resulted in the establishment of the Cairngorms Partnership Board (CPB) with representatives from local, national and international interests in the area.

In addressing the requirements of a management strategy the CWP suggested three altitudinal zones :

1   The mountain and plateau zone: above the former natural tree line (about 600m.).

2   The forest and moorland zone: the middle elevations of semi-natural and planted woodlands, moorlands and bogs between the mountain and plateau zone and the valley zone. Woodlands are mainly confined below the 600 m. contour.

3   The valley zone: the diverse, largely man-made environments of farmland, meadows, plantation forests and human settlements as well as the more natural river, loch, moor and semi-natural woodlands dispersed among these (generally lying below 300 m. in Strathspey and below 425 m. in upper Avonside and upper Deeside).

This chapter is concerned primarily with the ecology of the woodlands of the forest and valley zones but there are interactions with the mountain and plateau zones and with moorland, with many 'woodland' organisms foraging outside the woodlands. The interactions between moorland, semi-natural and plantation woodland, bogs, wetlands and riparian areas are complex and dynamic. Woodlands cover about 61,400 ha or 11.8% of the Cairngorms.

Local Actions

The Biodiversity Action Plan Steering Group developed guidance for the production of Local Biodiversity Action Plans (LBAPs) (Government Report 1995). LBAPs are intended to focus resources to conserve and enhance the biodiversity resource by means of local partnerships, taking account of both national and local priorities to deliver the objectives of national HAPs and SAPs at a local level. It is assumed that Local Authorities will usually lead and that the process will be linked to local or national funding to stimulate the interest of land managers.

   The Government has also recommended that plans be developed for Prime Biodiversity Areas (PBA). These are areas where concentrations of high priority habitats occur. The Cairngorms is an example of such an area and a recommendation has been made by RSPB to the CPB for the approval of the development of a LBAP for the Cairngorms. An early requirement of such a plan is an audit of species and habitats present in the Cairngorms, and local actions will need to be developed for priority species and habitats (*pers. comms*: Clifton Bain, RSPB; Janet Adamson, CPB).

   The development of a Woodland Biodiversity Action Plan (WBAP) at Rothiemurchus was considered to be an effective way of determining priorities on an individual estate basis. The objective of the Rothiemurchus WBAP is to describe the strategy and tactics for assessing, maintaining and increasing biodiversity within the forest. A preliminary audit of priority species has been conducted and some actions considered necessary to safeguard them have been identified. It is hoped that this plan will complement the development of a LBAP for the Cairngorms PBA, and that it will provide some guidance for the preparation of WBAPs in other areas.

A vision for the future

The CWP considered that the full range of forest ecosystems – from the mainly deciduous riverine woodland of willow, alder and oak in the valleys through the native pine and birch woods on the intermediate ground to the birch and juniper scrub at the tree-line – should be represented in the Cairngorms:

> We recommend that over time all existing native woodland should be conserved, improved and extended to provide long term environmental, recreational and timber benefits. This strategy will create a mosaic of native woodland interspersed with heather moorland, grassland, peatland and wetland and, on the lower ground in particular, agricultural land and productive forest of native and non-native species. Heather moors will still be extensive in some parts and used for grouse shooting and open hill deer stalking with the higher grassland areas being important as deer summering grounds. The proposed forest expansion should take place over a very long time-scale of more than 100 years with perhaps half occurring in the first 50 years. The natural heritage, employment, tourism, sport, wildlife and the owners of the land should all benefit greatly from the major changes proposed. (CWP, 1992)

The CPB draft strategy for Badenoch and Strathspey (Cairngorms Partnership, 1996), identifies two time spans, 20–25 years and 100–200 years:

> In the former we envisage achieving the consolidation and regeneration of existing native woodlands to guarantee their future. This will include the restructuring of plantations to create a more diverse age structure and range of native species. In the longer term we envisage that a substantial amount of new regenerated native woodland will have matured and new woodlands will be established where parent trees are no longer present, thus linking and expanding those woodlands that already exist. This will create extensive areas of interconnected woodland which will provide the base for a thriving sustainable forestry industry, recreation and tourism, as well as extensive areas of natural forest ecosystems.

The draft strategy highlighted the following aspects of forest management in order to achieve their vision:

1 native species predominating
2 a sustainable source of timber
3 a presumption in favour of natural means
4 increased biodiversity

5   increased opportunities for outdoor recreation
6   forestry techniques that are sensitive to the wildlife importance of
    woodlands, as well as the quality and quantity of fresh water
7   consideration of the impact of woodland siting and management on the
    landscape and views.

7.1: Rapid increase in seedling establishment and growth following a reduction in deer
numbers. *Photograph: P R Ratcliffe*

Our vision of the future forest should eventually be translated into a more
detailed description of the Desired Future Condition (DFC) (Ratcliffe and
Peterken, 1995). It should not be constrained by impressions of past eras of the
wildwood or particular periods of human occupancy, but should build on the
prehistoric and historic evidence, on recent experience and on future
expectations. We should plan to conserve the present range of species in
perpetuity, and to allow sufficient flexibility to enhance biodiversity and land-use
outputs in accordance with the wishes of future generations.

That our future management should be sustainable (in the widest sense; ie
including biodiversity, soil quality, timber production, economics, etc.) is the
only major constraint that we should work to.

Biodiversity

Biodiversity describes the variety of living things. Although here we are concerned primarily with the forest, there are a number of other ecosystems which are integral or adjacent to this, such as the riparian, river and bog ecosystems. Ecotones, such as tree-lines, gullies and farmland boundaries add to the biodiversity of Rothiemurchus forest.

Biodiversity is about the diversity of species, within species (genetic variability) and of ecosystems. It is not simply about species numbers. The 'quality' of biological diversity is also important, and 'characteristic' species, which are specifically associated with particular ecosystems are more important than ubiquitous species. For example, manipulation of the forest to create more woodland edge may increase the number of edge species, and total species number. However, if this results in the decline of scarce or characteristic pine wood species, then it is unacceptable.

It is particularly important to conserve the habitats of 'keystone' species. These are species which have a degree of relevance to the ecosystem which is greater than their own contribution to biodiversity – for example: mycorrhizal fungi are vital to the productivity of many plants; decay organisms are vital to preparing the woody substrate for secondary attack by other organisms; and ants play a part in the dispersal of plant seeds.

Proposed increases in biodiversity should be carefully managed within the natural, chemical and physical constraints of the sites, and be consistent with the ecology of all of the woodlands, including non-native species and those managed for commercial objectives.

Biodiversity is difficult to measure, and there are few ecosystems where there are adequate species lists available, to say nothing of the genetic diversity. It is therefore, useful to try to conserve all of the components of ecosystems in an attempt to guarantee the continuing maintenance, or enhancement of biodiversity. For example, coarse woody debris (CWD) – moribund, dead and decaying wood, in the form of fallen branches, fallen trees and standing dead trees (snags) – is an important surrogate for a wide variety of epiphytes, invertebrates and decay organisms, and by safeguarding a range of stages of CWD it is likely that many of these organisms will also be safeguarded. The concept of managing biodiversity surrogates in a holistic way is very important in ecosystem management. However, without some knowledge of at least some of the requirements, of some of the species, it is rather difficult to proceed.

How can biodiversity be improved upon?

Although Rothiemurchus is one of the largest native forest remnants left in Britain, it actually represents a mosaic of small fragments of the post-glacial forest and it is this fragmentation that has resulted in losses in biodiversity. It seems likely, therefore, that a wide range of species will benefit from a reversal of fragmentation.

The importance of fragmentation to particular species is dependent on such ecological factors as their dispersal performance in relation to distances between habitat fragments, home range size, minimum viable population size, minimum patch size requirements and densities.

Some of the larger animals which are now extinct in Scotland almost certainly became so due to habitat fragmentation alone, or more likely in combination with persecution. This suggests that any reversal of fragmentation will improve conditions for these species should future decisions be taken to reintroduce them.

Developing a strategy for managing biodiversity

In developing a strategy which will maintain or enhance biodiversity on a working estate, it is important to ensure that the Desired Future Outputs (DFOs) from all current and potential land-uses are fully appraised during the process. These should be given careful consideration as the plan develops so that the WBAP becomes integrally linked with other aspects of estate planning, such as the Rothiemurchus Forestry Long Term Working Plan (Hackett, Milner and Orr, 1996).

It is important that woodland restoration does not proceed to cause the large scale demise of non-woodland ecosystems and land-uses, such as grouse moors and open range deer stalking. However, the extension and restoration of forests will frequently require a reduction in deer numbers, and thus in the scale of deer stalking activity. In some priority areas local and seasonal impacts from deer will need to be reduced to very low levels.

Biodiversity can be increased in riparian areas by restoring native woodlands adjacent to rivers and their tributaries and this can also enhance the productivity of fish populations and aquatic life. In this way the recreational and social benefits associated with fishing, as well as the biological benefits, can be increased.

A number of species of conservation importance are dependent on non-woodland habitats, while others benefit from the woodland/non-woodland mosaic. It is therefore of paramount importance that the woodland expansion envisaged is located in the optimum places, and that the important species in all habitats benefit if possible. In order to minimise adverse impacts on non-woodland habitats, woodland expansion must be limited and, in this context, the provision of corridors connecting isolated fragments is considered to be valuable.

Forest Habitat Networks

A Forest Habitat Network (FHN) (Peterken, Baldock and Hampson, 1995) provides a means of increasing the area of habitats for a range of woodland species while minimising the adverse impacts on non-woodland land-uses and ecosystems. The FHN allows the development of a landscape mosaic which optimises opportunities for species requiring large habitat patches simply by increasing patch size. But more importantly it links patches together to increase the *effective* area of available habitat while minimising encroachment onto non-woodland areas. In addition it permits the dispersal and movement of a wide range of species over both short and long distances.

The degree to which woodland types will influence the presence and dispersion of organisms within them is highly dependent upon the size of patch relative to the ranging and dispersion distances of the particular species. For example, small patches may provide all of the requirements of immobile, 'old-growth' invertebrates, while they simply represent edge to wide ranging mobile species. The need for large patches of contiguous habitat is therefore likely to be far more important to large, wide ranging woodland specialists, than to small immobile ones.

Given that any expansion of forests in the Cairngorms should occur over a long time scale (c.100 years), patch sizes which are big enough to accommodate a wide range of extant and extinct species should be planned for. This will result in the provision of extended habitats for currently sensitive, rare or threatened species as well as for potential reintroductions. The socio-economic climate may never be appropriate for the reintroduction of some species but, by providing continuous (in time) and contiguous (in space) habitats at the appropriate scale, we are providing the choice for future generations, while not compromising current needs.

Against the potential benefits of increasing connectivity there are some disadvantages. Increased gene flow between habitat patches could reduce the adaptive fitness of the previously isolated populations. In addition, corridors can facilitate the spread and colonisation of unwanted species such as the grey squirrel and Japanese sika deer. Grey squirrels are present on lower Deeside while sika deer populations occur at a number of locations around the Cairngorms. The nearest sightings of sika deer to Rothiemurchus have been near Kingussie. However, there is already sufficient cover to allow the spread of sika deer into Strathspey, and the high proportion of conifers in the forests of upper Deeside seem to have prevented rapid colonisation by grey squirrels.

Clearly, the likely benefits from providing corridors or networks are very dependent upon a knowledge of the species being targeted and the pluses and minuses need to be carefully considered. However, the benefits usually seem to outweigh the disadvantages.

Woodland types present in Rothiemurchus

A classification of woodland types, which reflects the requirements of important species, has been proposed for the Cairngorms (Ratcliffe, Peterken and Hampson, 1998). These types are associated with specialised flora and fauna, and the degree to which these types, and 'old-growth' core areas, for example, can 'export' species and genotypes to other forest types is of great importance in landscapes with a high anthropogenic element. All of these seven forest types occur in Rothiemurchus.

1   Riparian woodland

Woodland and scrub on floodplains, beside rivers and along low level flush zones. Soils under the influence of a high watertable, but usually well-drained in the surface horizons. This type may also include secondary birch woodlands, alder/sallow scrub, birch and pine scrub on acid mires and pine/alder mixtures .

2   Mesic broadleaved woodland

Oak/ash/elm/hazel woodlands on base-rich soils, usually on well drained soils in the lowland zones. Most suitable ground is currently used for agriculture or habitation. May include secondary birch woodland. May also include pine woods on base rich soils.

3   Acid oak and birch woods

Oak/hazel and oak/birch woods on acid well drained soils. Virtually all survive in the lowland areas. Oak/pine woods are intermediate between this and the next type.

4   Pine, birch, juniper woodlands

Pine is the major constituent. Birch and juniper are usually present. Strongly associated with strongly acidic, podsolised soils and mire margins. Some examples are dominated by birch with no pine. In some pine woods juniper is locally dominant. Often appears as 'parkland' in mosaic with heaths. This type grades into sub-montane scrub. Bog forest (muskeg) is within this type but grades into riparian woods. Also intergrades with conifer plantations. Mixtures dominated by birch may be mainly birch/pine or birch/oak.

5   Sub-montane scrub

Scrub above the tree-line, intergrading with virtually all other types.

6   Coniferous plantation

Plantations usually established on heathy sites and former mires. Usually colonised by birch, rowan, alder and sallow. Occur in lowland, riparian to sub-montane zones.

7   Policy woodlands

Derived from plantations of a wide range of exotic species in nineteenth century or earlier.

7.2: A well established rowan seedling which has been repeatedly browsed by deer,
preventing it emerging from the surrounding heather canopy.
Photograph: P R Ratcliffe

Most of the preceding woodland types can be represented by different age and
growth stages. In terms of supporting different species of organisms, these
'structural types' are often of more significance than the particular species
composition of the woodland, though clearly these two factors interact. The main
structural types have been defined as follows:

1 Establishment

Most of the trees are less than 1 m. high and the field layer plants dominate.
Plant diversity and the degree to which this will support animals is heavily
dependent on the level of grazing intensity, usually from deer, sheep, hares and
rabbits. Many animals normally associated with open habitats are present.

2 Pre-thicket

This is the stage when trees are between 1 m. high and canopy closure. The tree
species are a more dominant component, influencing the microclimate and
subsequently the species which occur there. Grazing pressure is almost always
relatively low, enabling tree seedlings and saplings to put on height growth.
Woodland birds and insects colonise as patches develop from establishment to

pre-thicket. Large mammals which depend upon the availability of cover, such as roe deer, colonise.

3   Thicket

Most trees are between three and ten metres high. This stage follows canopy closure through to a rather ill-defined stage when the canopy becomes less dense, lower branches die and ground vegetation biomass begins to increase. Through much of this stage ground vegetation is patchy or non-existent due to the lack of light reaching the forest floor. During this stage edaphic factors, especially the water table, influence tree growth more strongly, and patches of different woodland and structural types can begin to develop, initiating the development of a complex mosaic of vegetation structure, which will ultimately form the mature forest with its intermix of dense trees, open muskegs, riparian areas, heaths and grasslands. Only woodland species will be associated with this stage, but patch size will influence the presence or absence of particular organisms.

4   Maturing

The trees are close to their ultimate height. The canopy remains relatively 'closed', though increasing light reaches the ground, allowing an increase in ground vegetation. Limited regeneration of shade-bearers occurs in shaded patches. Open patches will occur and light-demanders will regenerate into these gaps if they are big enough (c.>0.5 ha). Many trees will be producing seed, which will support increasing numbers of seed-eating animals, and their predators and parasites. In managed stands of trees, some thinning will be occurring in this stage, and some patches will be clear-felled, making way for the beginning of a further Establishment stage.

5   Old-growth

The ultimate height of trees is achieved, though trees may continue to grow slowly, increasing in girth. Some large trees will have blown down, or died *in situ* and fallen branch-wood will be considerable, heralding a substantial increase in amounts of CWD. There will be significant gaps in the canopy, adding to the complexity of the mosaic. There will be a well developed, multi-layered understorey. The availability of a wide range of ecological niches, especially those associated with CWD, will support a wide range of specialist species.

Biodiversity conservation

The general principle of conserving all of the components of an ecosystem, and the use of 'surrogates', to safeguard specific elements or species was made earlier. The reason for this approach is because our knowledge of ecosystems is incomplete both in terms of function and species composition, and that it is exceedingly difficult to manage an ecosystem based only on the individual needs of a few species (often the charismatic mega-fauna). Management becomes especially difficult when conflicts arise between the needs of different species.

However, although it is impossible to consider the specific requirements of all species in an ecosystem, it is difficult to progress the application of theories and generalisations (for example on habitat fragmentation and connectivity) to the real world, without considering species. But, which ones?

The approach adopted here is based on the selection of a number of sensitive, rare and threatened species in Rothiemurchus. After considering their detailed requirements in terms of patch size, dispersal distance, habitat requirements, etc., ecological similarities were identified in an attempt to link these together and 'rebuild' the ecosystem approach based on surrogate habitat components to the mutual benefit of most if not all of the species.

The emphasis has been to concentrate on the relatively rare, threatened and characteristic species of some of the important woodland types in the Cairngorms. The justification for this does not imply any disregard for common species, but these species are, by definition, most at risk and therefore most in need of positive management.

The species fall into two main types: the large, wide-ranging animals with rather narrow niche requirements, such as capercaillie and red squirrel; and those sedentary plants and animals with poor powers of dispersal and narrow niche requirements such as the ancient woodland plants, saproxylic invertebrates and soil microfauna. The main requirements of the former group is for sufficiently large areas of suitable habitat within their home ranges; the spatial distribution of habitat patches and the structure of woodlands are usually more important than tree species. The latter group require habitat connections which will allow relatively free exchange between sub-populations, when these are sufficiently small to present a risk of extinction should environmental changes occur, or if the habitat patch becomes reduced in size. Conversely, isolation may be desirable where sub-populations are of a viable size and where local genotypes are evolving. These species may require particular woodland types or growth stages, or be dependent on particular tree species. Any kind of woodland may not be acceptable.

Large animals are often 'keystone' species and they may be critical for the maintenance of biodiversity. It is, therefore, wise to prioritise their conservation. In Scotland, the large carnivores which were characteristic of upland woodlands are now extinct, but the largest extant species can be considered in the same way. Candidate species might therefore be the golden eagle, osprey, pine marten and wild cat. However, these species are relatively catholic in their requirements and they appear to thrive in a range of ecosystems. Indeed, they appear to benefit from a mosaic of habitat types. Large ungulates can be equally important and an appropriate level of grazing by red and roe deer is important in shaping a woodland structure which will benefit a number of the important pinewood species.

Native pinewoods (pine-birch-juniper woodlands) are the most extensive woodland type in the Cairngorm area. They form the main forest matrix throughout the Spey valley and are the most widespread woodland type at Rothiemurchus. Consequently, this woodland type has been targeted rather more intensively than other woodland types.

The species

The species were selected as objectively as possible by linking species of conservation importance – identified by the UK Biodiversity Action Plan process (Government Report, 1995) – with particular woodland habitats (see also Gibbons et al, 1995). Subsequently, the Invertebrate Site Register for Rothiemurchus (SNH), Freeman (1995) and Edgar (1995) were used to confine the list to those *likely* to be found at Rothiemurchus, and to add important species not so far selected. In addition, species specialists were approached to identify gaps and to provide autecological information.

However, it is important to note that the reason for using surrogates as a means of conserving biodiversity is based on the fundamental principle that we cannot expect to acquire the knowledge required for the conservation of every species of concern, and therefore any species list can only represent a part (hopefully a representative part) of the overall biodiversity. It is also impossible to specify in detail which species actually occur within the estate boundaries of Rothiemurchus, nor is it considered particularly helpful to do so. This is because biological recording has not been focused within the estate boundary, but rather more on the parts of Rothiemurchus which occur within the SSSIs and within the Cairngorms NNR, which include substantial amounts of non-wooded habitats. Equally, the selection of species is biased to those which occur in pinewoods and this may result in the omission of some species which are associated predominantly with woodland ecotones which intergrade into other habitats such as wetlands. For example, the rare dragonflies, *Aeschna caerulea, Somatochlora arctica* and *Coenagrion hastulatum* which breed in the forest mires and lochans, have been omitted from consideration here.

The selection of species is also influenced by different classifications of species into categories such as rare, sensitive, threatened and local. For example, eleven invertebrate RDB species and 84 notable species have been found in the North Rothiemurchus SSSI, and the area is rated as of Regional Importance by the British Lichen Society (Freeman, 1995). Clearly all of these species could not be considered here, but this classification has provided a relatively objective means of simplifying the list to a workable number of representative species.

This work was developed concurrently with that of Ratcliffe, et al (1999) and the same methodology used. The species accounts are presented without justifying all statements with references, for clarity. Full references are available in Ratcliffe, et al (1999).

1 *Formica aquilonia* (Scottish wood ant)

Current status: Widespread and locally abundant in the Highlands, but severe declines have been reported in some areas during the past twenty years. Listed by IUCN as threatened. Ants disperse a large number of forest plants, and are therefore keystone species.

Causes of loss or decline relevant to habitat connectivity: The replacement of open, traditionally managed woodlands by more dense plantations or thickets has created dark unsuitable conditions. The most vulnerable of the three ant species to fragmentation due to difficulty in dispersing over long distances.

Habitat requirements: Usually closely related to trees and sheltered areas in undisturbed open woodland. Thrives in woodlands with a diverse and open structure with glades. All three ants require arboreal aphids for food.

Minimum patch size: not known but said to be larger than for *F. exsecta* or *F. lugubris*. 5-10 ha?

Mobility and dispersal potential: possibly c.100m. *F. aquilonia* is very loyal to the vicinity of the nest site and new colonies usually occur close to their parents, thus having low colonising ability.

2   *Formica exsecta* (narrow headed ant)

Current status: Localised, but widely distributed in Europe, it has been recorded in lowland heathland in southern England and in native pinewoods in Scotland. Historical records in Scotland are from mid-Strathspey, Easter Ross and Rannoch. Scottish populations are currently known to exist in Glen More, at Abernethy and Carrbridge. Eighty nests were located in a recent survey. The species has experienced a dramatic decline throughout its range, with many sites lost in the Spey valley. It is listed as endangered on the GB Red List.

Causes of loss or decline relevant to habitat connectivity: Habitat fragmentation leading to potential inbreeding and loss of reproductive fitness has occurred. Intensive management of moorlands for deer and gamebirds, and the loss of semi-natural pine habitats have also contributed to their decline. They appear to be intolerant of human disturbances.

Habitat requirements: Sunny edges and clearings in pine woods (usually their southern aspects). Vegetation below 40cm high is favoured. Nests are often amongst heather, but grassy sites are probably suitable. The presence of relatively isolated shrubs of juniper, oak birch and gorse in clearings seems to be important.

Minimum patch size: Preference for sunny glades enables this species to use edges, and therefore to make use of relatively small patches with a large edge to interior ratio. Not known, 5 ha?

Mobility and dispersal potential: This species seems more able to move sites than does *F. aquilonia* or *F. lugubris*, but major changes to the surrounding habitat can leave them with no options. It is well adapted to the temporal dynamics of woodland structure, and can exploit clearings and glades caused by disturbances. The distance that queens will disperse from one nest to another, how they select a site on which to land and the circumstances under which they will found a new colony are not known.

3   *Formica lugubris* (northern wood ant)

Current status: Localised, but widely distributed in northern Europe. Locally distributed in the pinewoods of Speyside.

Causes of loss or decline relevant to habitat connectivity: Unknown.

Habitat requirements: Similar to *F. aquilonia* but in Finland found to be more common in younger forests with more open canopies and closer to forest edges.

Minimum patch size: Probably smaller than for *F. aquilonia*; c.5 ha? In Finland, has benefited from some fragmentation.

Mobility and dispersal potential: Primarily disperses by queens flying to new sites and colonising by nest parasitism or by founding a new nest. Therefore, good dispersal prospects and an ability to colonise young growth. c.2 km.

4   *Blera fallax* (a hoverfly)

Current status: Rare. In Scotland known only from Speyside on the basis of one adult and one puparium.

Causes of loss or decline relevant to habitat connectivity: not known

Habitat requirements: breeds in water filled holes in decaying pine stumps and roots. Suspect that pine stumps remain in a suitable state over long periods, and that it can remain in the same stump for several generations.

Minimum patch size: not known

Mobility and dispersal potential: not known

5   *Callicera rufa* (a hoverfly)

Current status: Rare. Recorded from about thirty 10km squares in the UK since 1990.

Causes of loss or decline relevant to habitat connectivity: Not known

Habitat requirements: Breeds in tree rot holes and water-filled decaying stumps in Scots pine and occasionally larch. Not found in trees less than approximately 100 years old. Can occur in suitable trees in non-woodland locations, ie roadsides.

Minimum patch size: Probably an individual tree.

Mobility and dispersal potential: Good. Probably approximately 5 km.

6   *Osmia uncinata* (a bee)

Current status: A recent addition to the British list and poorly known. Mainly recorded in the Spey valley between Kincraig and Nethy Bridge. A major host of the rare cleptoparasitic wasp, *Chrysura hirsuta.*

Causes of loss or decline relevant to habitat connectivity: loss of native pinewood.

Habitat requirements: Open, sunny and floristically rich sites (especially *Lotus corniculatus*).

Minimum patch size: unknown

Mobility and dispersal potential: unknown

7   *Chrysura hirsuta* (a wasp)

A rare cleptoparasitic wasp parasitizing *Osmia uncinata* (see above). No further information.

8   *Clubonia subsultans* (a spider)

Current status: Widespread in Europe, but in the UK only known at Abernethy forest and near Coylumbridge in the Cairngorms, and the Blackwood of Rannoch.

Causes of loss or decline relevant to habitat connectivity: Loss of native pine forest

Habitat requirements: Found on bark, branches and in litter of Scots pine, and on juniper below pine trees.

Minimum patch size: Not known. 5 ha?

Mobility and dispersal potential: Unknown.

9   *Dipoena torva* (a spider)

Current status: Widely distributed in the native pine forests of Rannoch, Rothiemurchus and Abernethy. Apparently not recorded on Deeside.

Causes of loss or decline relevant to habitat connectivity: Loss of old and senescent trees providing suitably fissured bark and loss of an open woodland structure.

Habitat requirements: Fissures on the bark of Scots pine. Feeds on wood ants. Open diversely structured pine forests.

Minimum patch size: Not known. 5 ha?

Mobility and dispersal potential: not known

10   *Pelecopsis elongata* (a spider)

Current status: Well established in Rothiemurchus and Abernethy forest. Also recorded near Loch Rannoch. Widespread in Europe.

Causes of loss or decline relevant to habitat connectivity: Conversion of open pine forests to dense plantations is thought to be the main threat. Grazing to maintain an open structure is considered to be important.

Habitat requirements: Mainly in dry pine litter amongst rocks and on the lower branches of juniper.

Minimum patch size: Not known. 5 ha?

Mobility and dispersal potential: unknown

11   *Xylophagus cinctus* (a fly)

Current status: Rare. Known from about ten 10km squares in Scotland.

Causes of loss or decline relevant to habitat connectivity: unknown

Habitat requirements: Under the bark of recently fallen large Scots pine trunks, this species is a predator on the larvae of other Diptera and Coleoptera.

Minimum patch size: Probably about 10 ha, based on the requirement for a newly fallen large tree (>60 years old) about every three years.

Mobility and dispersal potential: About 5–10 km, based on current evidence of the species being found up to 45 km from native pinewoods, but with 'stepping-stones' of pine plantations interspersed between.

12   *Medetera exellens* (a fly)

Current status: Known from about twenty-five 10 km squares throughout the highlands, since 1990.

Causes of loss or decline relevant to habitat connectivity: not known.

Habitat requirements: Under the bark of small fallen Scots pine trees and larger branches. Found in Scots pine plantations of about 30 years old and in mixed woods where pine is not always dominant.

Minimum patch size: Probably about 2.5 ha.

Mobility and dispersal potential: Probably at least 5–10 km.

13   *Loxia scotica* (Scottish crossbill)

Current status: This is the only species of bird which is considered to be endemic to the UK. However, there is confusion over the taxonomic position with regard to common and parrot crossbills and it is not always afforded full species status. It is mainly confined to native pinewoods or old established plantations. Recent reports suggest that there about 1,500–2,500 individuals in the UK, but numbers seem to fluctuate widely between years and counting is made difficult due to large irruptions of common crossbills from the continent. It is listed in Annex 1 of the EC Birds Directive and Appendix II of the Berne Convention. It is protected under the Wildlife and Countryside Act, 1981.

Causes of loss or decline relevant to habitat connectivity: None known.

Habitat requirements: Pinewoods with high structural diversity.

Minimum patch size: Not known. 25 ha?

Mobility and dispersal potential: Not known, but thought to be highly mobile.

7.3: The highest natural tree-line in Scotland at Creag Fhiaclach, Rothiemurchus (c. 600m).
Stunted native Scots pine. *Photograph: P R Ratcliffe*

14   *Parus cristatus* (crested tit)

Current status: A localised breeding population occurs in the Moray catchment and Speyside. The species is widely distributed in Europe, but the Scottish population is considered to be a separate race, *P. cristatus scoticus*. The total Scottish population was estimated to be 885 breeding pairs in 1979–80 based on densities of 0.01 breeding pairs/ha in plantations and 0.15/ha in open pine forest.

Causes of loss or decline relevant to habitat connectivity: Unknown, but their absence on Deeside could possibly be due to lack of connectivity. Past replacement of semi-natural pine woods with plantations, and intensive management causing a decline in the shrub layer and availability of suitable stumps in which to nest, could have had an effect.

Habitat requirements: Tall, bushy heather in open pine forests. The old pinewoods of Rothiemurchus, Abernethy and Glen More carried the largest populations during the early 1970s, and probably still do, where they will nest almost to the tree line. Forests derived from plantations, which provide a similar structure to semi-natural woods, with a well developed shrub layer are frequented in the lower Spey valley, and nest boxes are used. The most favoured habitats in a range of ten Scottish woods included, few small trees, high numbers of stumps for nest sites, a virtual absence of birch, high field layer diversity and hummocky ground. A strong association between crested tits and dead wood on standing trees has been demonstrated. Dead stumps (snags) more than 22 cm diameter and higher than 0.5 m are required for nesting, and nests are seldom more than four metres above the ground.

Minimum patch size: 25 ha

Mobility and dispersal potential: Usually sedentary and will not disperse much more than about 2 km from their nest site. However, in years when surplus birds are present, following a succession of mild winters, longer dispersal may occur. Two birds were recorded at Linn of Dee which may have travelled through the Lairig Ghru (Grant, 1984).

15   *Tetrao urogallus* (capercaillie)

Current status: In Britain this bird is currently largely confined to the eastern highlands of Scotland. It became extinct in Scotland around 1770, but the population expanded after introductions in the nineteenth century, initially at Taymouth Castle in 1837, and their numbers seemed to fluctuate with the availability of habitat up to about 1960. A tenfold decline in numbers has occurred over the past 20–30 years and numbers are considered to be around 2,000 birds at present.

Causes of loss or decline relevant to habitat connectivity: A reduction in the availability of open semi-natural pine forest is considered to be at least partially responsible for the current decline. Many birds have been killed by flying into deer fences, and this mortality may also be contributing to their decline.

Habitat requirements: Open woodland of Scots pine with large, old 'granny' trees and an abundant field layer of blaeberry and heather are favoured, although some colonisation of planted forests of spruce and other tree species has occurred in recent years. Indeed, plantation forests can provide suitable habitat for capercaillie if they are managed to provide a structure which simulates the open pine woods.

Minimum patch size: 500 ha. The smallest unit for management should be about 300-400 ha based on one lek, but a minimum of 1000 ha, of not necessarily continuous forest, is necessary to support a viable population.

Mobility and dispersal potential: Some hens are known to have moved over 20km during juvenile dispersal. They are thought to be able to disperse over relatively large distances across unsuitable habitat (K Duncan, *pers.com.*).

16   *Sciurus vulgaris* (red squirrel)

Current status: Within the UK the species has shown a reduction in numbers and range over the last 50 years and large populations are now confined largely to Scotland, which holds about 75% of the UK population (an estimated 120,000 animals) (JNCC, 1996). This reduction has been consistent with an increase in the range of grey squirrels (*Sciurus carolinensis*). Red squirrels are widely distributed in the Speyside area, mainly in pinewoods. Grey squirrels have been present in lower Deeside for some years now but do not seem to be extending their range substantially.

Causes of loss or decline relevant to habitat connectivity: The spread of grey squirrels, habitat fragmentation and disease. Red squirrels appear to be unable to compete with greys in woodlands with large proportions of large-seeded broadleaved trees. Large unfragmented blocks of mixed conifer forest are considered to be the most suitable habitat for red squirrels in Britain.

Habitat requirements: Large tracts of coniferous forests. Mixtures of conifers provide more continuous food supplies than single species. Seems to thrive in relatively smaller woodlands in the absence of grey squirrels.

Minimum patch size: Minimum viable areas and population sizes are not known but some areas exceeding 2,000 ha should be aimed for, even though some Scottish populations persist in smaller areas.

Mobility and dispersal potential: Little understood, but open land or conifer forest buffer zones of at least 3 km will deter or prevent grey squirrels colonising. It is not clear whether we can infer similar distances to reds.

17   *Castor fiber* (European beaver)

Current status: Extinct in Britain since sixteenth century. Serious declines throughout Europe have been countered by re-introduction programmes (eg in Norway, Poland, Holland and France). Scottish Natural Heritage are investigating the feasibility of reintroducing the species to Scotland (SNH, 1996).

Causes of loss or decline relevant to habitat connectivity: Habitat destruction, river pollution and hunting.

Habitat requirements: Riparian broadleaved woodland. Unpolluted water with abundant herbaceous vegetation for summer food and trees (aspen and willow are preferred) for winter food. The most suitable sites in Scotland for the reintroduction of beavers appear to be the Ness, Tay, Spey and Dee catchments.

Minimum patch size: c. 5km^2

Mobility and dispersal potential: Young *Castor canadensis*, the North American beaver, disperse up to 5 km from the natal nest. European beavers range from 0.5–12.8 km along river banks depending on forage availability, feeding primarily within about 60 m. of the waters edge. They do not seem to disperse across open country away from water courses.

18   The characteristic pinewood plants: creeping lady's tresses *(Goodyera repens),* twinflower (*Linnaea borealis*) and one flowered wintergreen (*Moneses uniflora*).

Current status: All are rare.

Causes of loss or decline relevant to habitat connectivity: Fragmentation and isolation of habitats.

Habitat requirements: Largely restricted to pinewoods. All are mycorrhizal and all require damp conditions.

Minimum patch size: Unknown.

Mobility and dispersal potential: Most spread is by vegetative means, which limits their ability to spread to connected areas of suitable habitat. The seed producing component of populations is very small, but perhaps small amounts of seed produced sporadically could provide adequate dispersal if suitable habitats are available. It follows that the more fragmented the habitat the less becomes the probability of seeds encountering favourable conditions. It seems, therefore, that dispersal distances should be assumed to be rather small.

7.4: A previously suppressed Scots pine sapling with multiple leading shoots due to repeated browsing by deer. Recent reductions in deer numbers have allowed a rapid increase in growth. *Photograph: P R Ratcliffe*

19   The aspen saproxylic insect community (Table 1).

Current status: The first species (Table 1) is new to science, the second is a new record in Britain and the next six are Red Data Book Species. The remainder are all 'Notable' species. Aspen woods are a scarce resource in highland Scotland (total area of 157 ha), and woods larger than 1ha are largely confined to the Spey valley between Newtonmore and Grantown-on-Spey. Consequently any species dependent on aspen are likely to be under threat. The saproxylic species listed have not been recorded on other species of tree. Not all the species in Table 1 have been recorded at Rothiemurchus, but small areas of aspen are present.

Causes of loss or decline relevant to habitat connectivity: Possibly loss of habitat and fragmentation.

Habitat requirements: Moist, rotting cambium of dead aspen.

Minimum patch size: About 2 ha. Woods of less than 1 ha are usually poor in saproxylic invertebrates. Woods larger than 4.5 ha are required to support the full range of species.

Mobility and dispersal potential: Possibly relatively mobile in terms of moving through adjacent wooded habitats, though unlikely to be able to traverse more than about 1 km through very hostile (non-wooded) habitats.

Table 1: The aspen saproxylic insect community of conservation significance in the Cairngorms

	Status
Ecataetia spp (a fly)	New species
Mycetobia obscura (a fly)	New species to Britain
Hammerschmidtia ferruginea (a hoverfly)	RDB 1 (Endangered)
Homalocephala albitaris (a fly)	RDB 1
Strongylophthalmyia ustulata (a fly)	RDB 1
Tachypeza heri (a fly)	RDB 2 (Vulnerable)
Tachypeza truncorum (a fly)	RDB 3 (Rare)
Medetera inspissata (a fly)	RDB 3
Gnophomyia viridipennis (a fly)	Notable (Occurrence in 16-100 10 km grid squares)
Clusoides apicalis (a fly)	Notable
Stegena coleoptera (a fly)	Notable
Lonchaea peregrina (a fly)	Notable
Systenus pallipes (a fly)	Notable
Xylota tarda (a fly)	Notable
Criorhina ranunculi (a hoverfly)	Notable
Saperda carcharius (a beetle)	Notable

Further sensitive, rare and endangered species were identified from the Scottish Natural Heritage site registers for the National Nature Reserve and Sites of Special Scientific Interest (Table 2). These species do not necessarily occur in

Rothiemurchus but probably do so. There appears to be little autecological information on these species, and conservation management must rely on the precautionary principle to maintain suitable conditions until such information is available.

Table 2: Additional woodland species of conservation significance in the Cairngorms

Invertebrates

Acanthocinus aedilis	Timberman beetle	pine
Thanasimus rufipes	Chequered beetle	pine
Rhizophagus parvulus	a bark beetle	
Ostoma ferrugineum	saproxylic beetle	pine
Chrysanthia nigricornis	saproxylic beetle	pine
Chamaesyrphus caledonicus	a hoverfly	pine
Chamaesyrphus scaevoides	a hoverfly	pinewoods
Rhyacionia duplana	Elgin shoot moth	pinewoods

Fungi

Boletus flavidus	pinewoods
Collybia aceroata	
Cortinarius pinicola	
Lactarius hysginus	
Lactarius musteus	
Mycena purpurofolia	
Russula paludosa	
Russula virosa	
Tricholema albobunneum	
Tricholema equestre	
Tricholema focale	

Lichens

Calicion hyperelli	pinewoods
Calicium spp.	
Chaenotheca spp.	
Xylographa spp	

Analysis of the species data

The species selected are presented in Table 1, along with a summary of the autecological data relevant to their association with woodland cover and structure. It is clear that, for a number of the important species, there is insufficient data on which to base firm recommendations for their conservation, and it is necessary to invoke the precautionary principle to ensure that as far as is possible these species do not decline further. In many cases the only recommendation can be to ensure the long term future of the necessary habitat conditions. However, there are a number of clues as to how this might be taken forward. For many of the smaller, less mobile animals this means ensuring continuity of open diverse pinewood habitats, and trying to ensure that they are able to disperse freely into acceptable habitats.

Table 3: Summary of data for selected species

Species	Dispersal distance	Minimum patch size	Habitat	Grazing required
ANTS				
Scottish wood ant	100m	5–10 ha	open pine	some
narrow-headed ant	2 km	5 ha	sunny glades	some
northern wood ant	2 km	5 ha	open pine	some
HOVERFLIES				
Blera fallax	?	? 1 tree	pine rot hole	-
Callicera rufa	c. 5 km	? 1 tree	pine rot hole	-
BEES & WASPS				
O. uncinata				
C. hirsuta				
SPIDERS				
Clubonia subsultans	?	? 5 ha	open pine	some
Dipoena torva	?	? 5 ha	open pine	some
Pelecopsis elongata	?	? 5 ha	open pine	some
FLIES				
Xylophagus cinctus	5-10 km	10 ha	pine bark	-
Medetera exellens	5-10 km	2.5 ha	pine bark	-
BIRDS				
Scottish crossbill	v. high	?c.25 ha	pinewoods with high structural diversity	some
crested tit	2 km	25 ha	open pine, tall heather, snags	reduced grazing beneficial
capercaillie	20 km	500 ha	open pine, old trees, diverse shrub layer	some
MAMMALS				
red squirrel	1-2 km	100/2000 ha	mixed conifers	-
beaver	5 -12 km	500 ha	riparian broadleaved woods	-

PINEWOOD PLANTS

creeping lady's tresses   {All these have limited powers of
twinflower   {dispersion and spread mainly
one flowered wintergreen   {vegetatively

Common factors

Although there is a notable lack of information, certain important common factors emerge from an analysis of the species accounts. Several species seem unable to disperse much more than a distance of 1-2 km, and some areas of contiguous woodland, which are larger than the needs of the species with the largest minimum patch size, appear to be important.

Red squirrel and capercaillie require some patches larger than 500 ha. Red squirrels may be able to cope better than capercaillie in areas as small as 100 ha as long as sufficient suitable habitat occurs within 2 km of the patch. Both species seem to benefit when maximum distances between patches do not exceed 2 km. Scottish crossbills, crested tits and Scottish wood ants also appear to benefit from this pattern. Some patches can be smaller, but it seems that virtually all pinewood species will benefit from patches larger than 5 ha.

Many species require pinewoods with an open structure and a diverse herb and shrub layer, which in many places is maintained by a low level of grazing, usually by deer. A large number of species require dead wood, and it seems important to maintain continuity (in time) and contiguity (in space) of this habitat. The existing areas and structure of forest in Rothiemurchus appear to be sufficiently large to sustain red squirrel and capercaillie, and patches seem to be sufficiently close to each other to allow movement. There is much to be gained by maintaining existing links and in establishing new ones.

Developing the Desired Future Condition

Small scale lack of continuity may be limiting the expansion of some of the more sedentary species such as the saproxylic fauna and the key species of ants and spiders. The main requirement here is to establish new native woodland connections and attempt to restrict most gaps to less than 1 km. There is an important need to establish and manage for continuity and contiguity of woodlands of an appropriate structure at this scale. Connections should be established, where existing woodland patches are isolated by distances greater than 1 km, by natural regeneration, where possible, but new planting may be necessary in some places. The planting of small patches of native woodlands in remote non-wooded areas can act as future seed sources for natural regeneration. This will help establish a temporal pattern of diversity.

The existing large forest areas should be maintained, and extended where appropriate to ensure continuity of habitat for the larger wide ranging species, specifically capercaillie and red squirrel. However, this should not be allowed to impact seriously on other land-uses such as deer stalking and grouse shooting, or on important non-wooded habitats. There should be a presumption against any further planting of large-seeded broadleaves to reduce the opportunities of grey squirrels colonising.

The extension linking of high altitude scrub tree-lines with lower ground at such places as Inshriach, Gleann Einich and the Lairig Ghru would provide benefits. Improved connectivity of the fragmented birchwoods along the Spey, from Spey Dam in the west to Glenbeg and Lettoch downstream of Grantown-on-Spey in the east, could provide important linked riparian habitats through Rothiemurchus. In some situations relatively large scale planting should not automatically be ruled out, especially in places where very long time scales may be required before natural woodland colonisation will occur. An alternative is to establish small exclosures of native tree species in such places to provide seed sources for future colonisation. Some replacement of farmland by woodlands may be inevitable; however, this is likely to be relatively small scale, and it should not be hurried. The time scale will to some extent allow people to adjust to the changes.

Management should continue with the objective of trying to maintain a 'normal' forest structure (Hackett et al, 1996), and it is important in the context of native woodland regeneration not to attempt to achieve large increases in woodland cover over too short a time period. A management mix of continuous cover, silviculture, and small scale clear-cutting will mimic natural disturbance regimes, and these methods should be used to complement each other in achieving an appropriate balance of age classes and woodland structure. The existing LTWP appears to provide the means to achieve this.

The important range of selected invertebrate species will clearly require continuity of habitats, but if they are to expand well beyond the minimum viable population size, linkages of old growth will be necessary. Old Growth Core Areas (OGCAs) could be established where no removal of timber would be permitted, which could be connected by Extended Rotation Areas (ERAs), where a proportion of trees are removed at a range of ages beyond normally accepted rotations. This should provide the necessary connections to allow populations to disperse from the OGCAs into the areas managed for timber production. ERA connectivity should be planned to prevent gaps of more than 1 km. This is as important for riparian woodlands as it is for native pinewoods. There is an important need to encourage the development of markets for big logs.

A large range of species require CWD in one form or another. Rot holes in tree stumps, humid and dry bark and dead wood in a variety of micro-climates provide habitats for a wide range of common and rare species (see Ratcliffe, 1993). Snags (standing dead trees with no top), more than 22 cm diameter and between 0.5–4.0 m tall are required as nesting sites for crested tits.

A recent survey (Hackett, 1996) has revealed rather low levels of CWD relative to what could be available in managed woodlands of these types. This may be restricting the viability of some species, and consideration should be given to increasing the amounts of dead wood. Removal of dead and fallen trees should be prevented and killing some trees by ring barking, and felling some trees from high stumps (c.>1.5 metres), could quickly increase the amounts of this important resource.

Many important species seem to require a habitat structure which will only be maintained in the presence of relatively low levels of grazing, or from some simulated management. Deer densities of 4–6 deer km^{-2} are compatible with the regeneration of native woodlands and would probably help maintain the conditions for many of the key species. The recent effects of reduced deer densities at Abernethy and Rothiemurchus support this. Clearly, the regulation of red deer densities at these levels will largely remove the need to fence against deer, achieving recreational, landscape and wildlife benefits, including the prevention of mortality of capercaillie, black grouse and other woodland birds caused by collisions with deer fences (Ratcliffe, 1998). The need to regulate the local and seasonal impact of deer may, however, require the use of temporary, small-scale fencing from time to time especially to protect sensitive species such as aspen, hazel and holly. The management of deer at Rothiemurchus is in close accordance with these requirements, and it is recommended that the current work to maintain deer densities at these levels is continued.

7.5: Holly (rare in Rothiemurchus) protected from deer browsing by dense juniper. Mature Scots pine in background. *Photograph: P R Ratcliffe*

Acknowledgements

This work has drawn heavily on a previous study commissioned by Scottish Natural Heritage (Ratcliffe et al, 1998), and on a study to develop a Woodland Biodiversity Action Plan for Rothiemurchus conducted for Finlayson-Hughes of

Inverness and funded by the Forestry Authority. Many people, too numerous to mention, helped me but I am especially grateful to David Carstairs and Keith Duncan (SNH, Achantoul), Dave Phillips (SNH, Edinburgh) and Iain MacGowan (SNH, Battleby) for their help in compiling the species lists and providing much autecological information. Mairi Cooper (SNH, Edinburgh) provided recent information on red squirrels and on the feasibility of reintroducing the beaver to Scotland. Clifton Bain (RSPB) and Janet Adamson (CPB) provided information on the development of the LBAP for the Cairngorms. Last, but not least, I thank Johnny and Philippa Grant for their warm hospitality during my visits to Rothiemurchus, and for the privilege of working in one of the finest natural environments in Scotland.

References

Cairngorms Partnership (1996) *Managing the Cairngorms – a consultation Paper. Badenoch and Strathspey.* The Cairngorms Partnership, Grantown-on-Spey.

Cairngorms Working Party (1992). *Common Sense and Sustainability : a Partnership for the Cairngorms.* The Report of the Cairngorms Working Party to the Secretary of State for Scotland. Scottish Office, Edinburgh.

Department of the Environment (1995) *The Habitats Directive: How it will apply in Great Britain.* DoE, London.

Edgar, A. (1995) Biological files search and data organisation. Cairngorms sub-area. *Unpublished Report to Scottish Natural Heritage, Strathspey*

Freeman, P. (1995) *Rothiemurchus. A Summary of its Ecological Interest.* Unpublished Report, Rothiemurchus.

Gibbons, D. W., Fisher, I. and Avery, M I (1995) *Linking species to habitats.* A Report of a Survey by the Biodiversity Challenge Group to English Nature.

Government Report (1994a) *Biodiversity: the UK Action Plan.* London, HMSO.

Government Report (1994b) *Sustainable Forestry: the UK Programme.* HMSO, London.

Government Report (1995) *Biodiversity: The UK Steering Group Report. Volume 1: Meeting the Rio Challenge. Volume 2: Action Plans.* HMSO, London.

Grant, J. P. (1984) Crested tits on Deeside. *Scottish Birds* 13, 54-55.

Hackett, A (1996) *Rothiemurchus Deadwood Survey Report.* Unpublished Report, Finlayson-Hughes, Inverness.

Hackett, A, Milner, N and Orr, D (1996) *The Forest of Rothiemurchus Long Term Working Plan.* Unpublished Report, Finlayson-Hughes, Inverness

JNCC (1996) *UK Strategy for red squirrel conservation.* Joint Nature Conservation Committee, Peterborough.

Loiskekoski, M., Mahonen, M., Puranen, R and Rizk, N. (1993) *Ministerial Conference on the Protection of Forests in Europe, 16-17 June 1993 in Helsinki* Ministry of Agriculture and Forestry, Helsinki.

Peterken, G. F., Baldock, D. and Hampson, A. (1995) A forest habitat network for Scotland. *Scottish Natural Heritage Research, Survey and Monitoring Report.* No 44.

Ratcliffe, P. R. (1993) *Biodiversity in Britain's Forests.* The Forestry Authority, Edinburgh.

Ratcliffe, P. R. (1997) Biodiversity, sustainability and silvicultural principles. In: Miller, H. G. *Plantation Forestry: A Sustainable Resource.* Institute of Chartered Foresters, Edinburgh, 34-44.

Ratcliffe, P. R. (1998) Woodland deer management: integrating the control of their impact with multiple objective forest management in Scotland. In : Goldspink, C. King, S and Putman, R. J. *Population Ecology, Management and Welfare of Deer.* Manchester Metropolitan University, Manchester. pp. 67-72.

Ratcliffe, P. R. and Peterken, G. F. (1995) The potential for biodiversity in British upland spruce forests. *Forest Ecology and Management.* 79, 153-160.

Ratcliffe, P. R., Peterken, G. F. and Hampson A. (1999). *A forest habitat network for the Cairngorms. Scottish Natural Heritage, Survey and Monitoring Report* No. 114. Edinburgh.

Scottish Natural Heritage (1996) Re-introduction of European beavers to Scotland. *Information and Advisory Note* 55. SNH, Edinburgh.

8. An Architectural and Decorative Appreciation of The Doune

Mary Tindall and Ian Gow

The Doune is a house we feel that we all know well, because of the very vivid word picture presented by Elizabeth Grant. Her words precisely fit the surviving structure and recreate the house on paper with a most enviable impressive precision. There is hardly a dull sentence in her book and, if you approach it as we have done, with a particular interest in interiors and architecture, the vivid descriptions supply vital documentation for changing customs and fashions. We can also relate her words to illustrations of similar things in other houses that no longer survive at the Doune. This is facilitated by her talent for description, honed by her many years of professional journalism. Yet the secret of her success in the *Memoirs* is perhaps that she had targeted an audience in her children and this brings it to life. It is not nostalgic, wallowing in memories of a lost childhood, but a very realistic assessment. It has the taint of a moral story for the instruction of the young.

Although it is a house we think we all know well, the story is more complicated than it appears because the very familiar photograph reproduced in the 1911 edition of the *Memoirs* shows the house before it had been altered during her brother's building campaign. This resulted in a much larger house, that was to prove unmanageable by the middle of the twentieth century.

The Doune has a wider interest because the Grants were people of fashion and were concerned – when they had the money – in keeping up with the latest trends. This was to be their undoing. Because the house was situated in the Highlands, we also have a strong sense of the challenge that these fashionable notions posed to the native genius of the place. The period around 1800 was one of profound change in the way people organised their houses. There had been a consumer revolution and many more things were available, leading to higher expectations. But there were also people like Elizabeth Grant's aunt, who were conscious that traditional values were under threat. Elizabeth Grant writes amusingly of how her aunt simply did not want to hear of these newfangled notions, because she thought they could only hasten the end of what had made Rothiemurchus most attractive and desirable.

If the primary source for the history of the Doune are the *Memoirs* themselves, they can now be related to the documentary history of the house in typescript abstract from the family muniments prepared by Jane Lindsay. Sadly, there are very few visual records or architectural designs to help us to grasp this story, and this dearth is the more tantalising because Elizabeth Grant makes clear that the Doune, as built, was but a part of her father's intentions. An essential characteristic of the Grant's architectural patronage was that they were themselves uncertain of quite where the design was leading. I think one of the most entertaining of her earliest memories of the Doune is of the quantities of building materials lying around.

We are going to begin, not at the historical origin of the house, but where the visual record begins. Obviously the Doune was a long-established inhabited site, but the first piece of visual evidence was a 'survey' of 1762 showing the entrance, or south-east front, which was not merely a survey but also incorporated suggestions for regularising the Doune. A surveyor, rather than an architect, suggested that the old house could be modernised by making it more classical in appearance. The standard problem that beset eighteenth century Scottish architects was in making something irregular look symmetrical. Here a standard solution has been adopted – an apparent regularity has been attempted by centralising the front door and by the addition of neat little flanking pavilions. It is quite certain that the door was never in this central position.

What is so remarkable about Elizabeth Grant's account is that her descriptions of the series of rooms occupied by the family can be related precisely to modern surveys. Elizabeth Grant describes how the State Bedroom lay through a room she called the Hall, with the family bedroom on the other side. These rooms can now be pinpointed. The eastern of the two pavilions is the squalid black kitchen, built of turf, where a mouse fell from the thatch into the soup. In the late eighteenth century, the classic way of gaining larger rooms – which were much in demand at this time when larger parties became fashionable – was to add pavilions flanking the existing house (that had been built at a time when people required a smaller scale, constricted, core). As photographs make clear, although the house was later to be changed considerably, we readily recognise the essence of the present house.

Although the plan of the Doune in the middle of the eighteenth century may appear to us today to be a muddle, this type of house was then not uncommon, and the small scale should not be read as a sign of a lack of sophistication or of informality. The Dalrymple family's farmhouse at North Berwick, for instance, shows how it was common in Scots architecture for a plain, but symmetrical exterior to mask an intricate asymmetrical internal plan, whose divisions were not necessarily reflected on the exterior. Like the Dalrymple's farmhouse, it is clear that the Doune had an ambitious first floor State apartment, the principal room of which would have been the formal dining room, as Elizabeth Grant describes.

Elizabeth Grant shows that, as in many Scottish houses, the apparently modest structure possessed ambitious furnishings. She makes it perfectly clear in her vivid description that the best green damask bed is a 'state bed', for the accommodation of their most important visitors, and was accompanied by fashionable japanned furniture, both of which may now seem unexpected in the

Highlands because we have forgotten how the Scots used to relish grand beds and rich upholstery. The most celebrated and sumptuous example is the Melville State Bed, now in the Victoria and Albert Museum. Our current ideas about Highland houses have been conditioned by the more home-spun later ethos of the mid-nineteenth century Scotch Baronial Revival, with its emphasis on native granite, Scots pine and the local fauna of mounted stags' heads.

The first growth away from this compact block to be described by Elizabeth Grant, was when her doctor grandfather added a grand new room in 1786 in a flanking pavilion built onto the western corner of the Old Doune. He was not to have long to enjoy the property. It must have been vaguely intended to balance the black kitchen on the eastern side. Behind much of the early architectural history of the Doune there is always the sense that, at some later stage, the whole is going to be balanced up.

8.1: The Doune of Rothiemurchus in 1878
Photograph: By kind permission of J P Grant of Rothiemurchus

If the first problem that beset the classical Scottish architect was to make an old irregular house symmetrical, the second problem that arose from adapting old fashioned buildings lay in their complicated floor levels. Although, by adding a new room in a detached pavilion, her grandfather was able to create a room with a much larger volume than could ever have been carved out of the old house with its historically smaller scale, his new addition inevitably involved a change of fashion away from the old-established idea of state floor at first, or *piano nobile*, level. To insulate the new room from damp, however, it was raised over a cellar approached by its own external stairway. Again, it is typical of these new fashionable ideas that the function of this large room was that of a still formal dining room – for which the cellar, approached by an external stair, was a very convenient adjunct.

The old and new floor levels were resolved by a turning stair – again precisely described by Elizabeth Grant. But the architectural result was to create an imposing new dining room, whose scale must have contrasted with the rooms within the Old Doune. Later architects had the challenge of trying to harmonise the old and new.

After her grandfather's tenure was cut short in 1790, it fell to her father to make sense of the hybrid unfinished house. He is always said to have acted as his own architect. Again, to a later generation this lack of professional advice contributes to the idea that the Doune was somehow 'home-spun', but it is worth bearing in mind contemporary improvements at neighbouring houses. Those at Balavil, or Belleville as it was then known, were carried out in 1792 to designs that had been prepared by Robert Adam, the leading architect in the land. These very architectural effects, if somewhat modified in execution, could hardly have been more prominent in the landscape given the exposed site of that house. It is interesting to see among Adam's designs now in the Soane Museum that he must have displaced a fashionable Edinburgh architect in this commission, because earlier designs bear a striking resemblance to 35 St Andrews Square. Another neighbouring house was the Duchess of Gordon's Kinrara. Although it may appear, by contrast with Balavil, to be innocent of an architect's advice – in the way that it is at one with the elemental landscape through the use of thatch and the tree-trunk verandahs – it is a pioneering essay in the late Picturesque style of architecture in the way it is opened up to the landscape with its large full length windows. We know that the Grants must have been aware of these new notions from the way Elizabeth Grant is conscious that her father's new drawing room, with its bow window, was carefully sited to command and enjoy the view. It would be wrong, therefore, to fall into the trap of assuming that the Spey valley was architecturally unsophisticated and ethnic in its tastes.

In the Doune of 1803 we can study the result of her father's earliest attempts to use up the building materials assembled for the purpose. One of his primary concerns, which was typical of late-eighteenth century efficient estate management, was to create a court of offices to give an orderly architectural expression to an enlightened concentration of the various domestic activities, where the landowner or manager could readily keep an eye on everything. At the Doune these activities had previously been carried out across the landscape in an unsightly, open heart surgery manner, with the laundry in the bushes, disfiguring the house's immediate environs. The strength of the desire to organise these activities centrally is perhaps reflected in the essential prerequisite of her father being obliged to cut back into the very earth-mound behind the house to the north, which gave the Doune its name. The building of the walled garden a few years earlier was a symptom of the same desire to zone and contain all the unsuitable activities that had been too visible from the public rooms of the old house to suit new late-eighteenth century notions of gentility.

This concentration of the offices contiguous to the Old Doune, however, must have contributed to a desire to re-orientate the public rooms alongside her grandfather's spacious new dining room and away from the old house which was so obviously losing status. This may have been the result of a series of piece-meal changes of mind: certainly analysis throws up a number of straight-joints where new structures have been abutted to the old. The bay of the extension to the north-west, behind her grandfather's dining room was strategically sited to command the prospect. Elizabeth Grant also makes quite clear that this new lop-sided house, with a new valency to the west, was intended to be balanced-up by the counterweight of a symmetrical new wing on the eastern side of the Old Doune.

A major innovation (as it proved the final event in the alterations of 1813), was the introduction of a new and principal staircase. It was to be of crucial importance in ironing out the different floor levels at the western (modern) end of the house. Elizabeth Grant is perhaps rather too severe a critic of her father's architectural abilities, since his design both respected what he found and was rather practical. The quoins on his father's dining room pavilion must have provided a key for new features like the rusticated entrance door. The bow gave a new spacious elegance to the rooms behind, while the Venetian door and window above must have lit the deeper circulation spaces of the entrance hall and stair effectively. The resulting austere plainness was not out of character with informed and fashionable 1790s taste in the South.

There had also been important changes in the function of the rooms c.1813, as the climax of what might be seen as her father's second phase of improvements. It is symptomatic of the Grant's fashionableness that the largest room in the extension (that was to become the New Doune), was the Library and that this was a new use for her grandfather's dining room – the largest room in the house with the tallest ceiling. To replace its original function, a new dining room had been built across the new stairhall with a bay window nodded to Picturesque notions and was carried-up to light a bedroom above. The best bedroom lay over the library. The New Doune, with its large rooms opened-up to the landscape, was thus quite different in both spirit and scale from the Old Doune.

Because of the house's later struggles with dry rot, only a little of the detail of the interiors is now visible, but the calibre of the plasterwork and woodwork shows the sophisticated internal elegance of the New Doune. The joiners for the all-important stair were brought from Perth. Although little of the decorative finishes and paintwork described by Elizabeth Grant are visible today, her vivid descriptions can be related to contemporary visual evidence from other houses which again attest to the up-to-date fashionableness of the result.

The Grant's library may have been in the Highlands but in its spirit it was perfectly attuned to fashionable Southern room usages. The idea of a library as a more comfortable and relaxed everyday living room – almost a family lounging room – was a fashionable Regency idea contrasting with the formal drawing room that had been developed and seemed so central to late-eighteenth century mores. The library requirement must have been precipitated by the arrival of the 'fine library' from Thorley Hall in Hertfordshire. The Grants' library also had tall bookcases made of local fir from the Rothiemurchus forest, relieved with black mouldings. Again, if this material sounds home-spun, it is worth remembering that the fashionable and contemporary English cabinet-makers, Bullock, whose patrons included the Duke of Atholl and Sir Walter Scott, had a predilection for local materials like the larch and Glen Tilt marble at Blair. The fir bookcases must also have served as an advert for the Grants' timber.

Almost every detail described by Elizabeth Grant of the fitting up of the library also reflected fashionable notions in its proto-antiquarian ornaments, eking out the standard classical fare of the busts ranged along the top of the tall cases, with Indian arrows and old weaponry. The hierarchical picture hanging at the Doune is a further indicator of Elizabeth Grant's acute powers of observation. The fashionably Antiquarian gloss on the character of the Grants' new library was followed through by the introduction of the portrait of 'a James the Sixth style of man… the only picture allowed in the room'. Because the tall bookcases in the Library diminished its potential for hanging pictures, in spite of its possessing the largest wall area in the house, the best of the cabinet pictures (from Thorley Hall) fell-out on the walls of the new dining room. The Grant family portraits, of lesser aesthetic value by contrast, were ranked on the high walls of her father's new staircase. It is a fascinating detail, and possibly a reflection on their lack of artistic pretensions, that she tells us that they were unframed.

It is interesting that, in spite of the attractions of the library (where Jane was to be married), her mother was anxious to recreate a drawing room in the bow-windowed room on the first floor (intended as a bedroom), over the dining room. Again this emphasis on the first floor must have made the new staircase yet more necessary and important.

In her rather acerbic description of her mother's decorations, Elizabeth Grant could not but betray the prejudices of a later early-Victorian quest for comfort, but again she is perhaps unconsciously describing fashionable effects from her parents' day, and the colour schemes which she thought 'not happily chosen' and 'cold looking' can be matched, precisely, with a very rare set of contemporary colour cards from the Agnew family papers in the Scottish Record Office (SRO).

With great precision we can match her description of the black lining creating fictive panelling on the Library walls – a fashionable look of brief duration that derived from the new connoisseurship of Greek vase painting, with the archaeological evidence that recently came to light in 13 Heriot Row, Edinburgh. Again, one is impressed both with the acuteness of the observation of a short-lived fashion and her total recall. This Regency look of Grecian black-lining copied from antique vases, picking up the black mouldings of the fir cases, may have been intended as a modernisation of her grandfather's Adamitic dining room. To our eyes, its Neo-Classical frieze is a thing of exceptional quality, with its cast vases, rinceau and honeysuckle ornaments, but to the younger generation, to which her parents belonged, it may have begun to appear insipid and thus they felt impelled to add heavier ornaments to the Adamitic library.

Her mother's upstairs drawing room, that had been intended as a bedroom, may have been architecturally less distinguished but strove at no less modish effects with 'Angelica Kauffmann's prints pinned to the walls', creating a fashionable print-room effect.

Although Elizabeth Grant is describing a particular house, the Doune can also be seen as a sort of weather-vane of prevailing fashions, by her observation that the new bedrooms were expensively and fashionably wall-papered while the less important rooms in the old house, by contrast, were merely distempered – again, like the pictures, creating a sense of hierarchy across the house. The papers may well have been as rich as the contemporary paper, lovingly preserved into the age of photography, at Culloden House in the mistaken belief that this had been Bonnie Prince Charlie's bedroom. If the Doune of her youth was austere by Elizabeth Grant's later early-Victorian notions of domestic comfort, by the standards of its own day it must have been both much more fashionable and luxurious than one might have thought.

The irony underlying this newly-created Highland luxury was that by 1827 they were not left with the means to maintain it, and Elizabeth Grant gives a moving description of their having to skulk amidst this splendour before the bailiffs moved in. One way out of their financial difficulties was to lie in a profound change in the perception of the Highlands. This was a result of a picturesque re-evaluation of Scotland which was to turn houses like the Doune, situated amid the most spectacular scenery that Scotland can offer, with sporting potential, into highly lettable assets attracting wealthy Southerners – an asset that was otherwise unrealisable because of the entail.

As Elizabeth Grant was well aware, they were exceptionally lucky in their tenant, the Duchess of Bedford, who was at one and the same time part of her childhood world while, through her friendship with Landseer, was part of this new vision of the Highland world. With a sensitivity to an aesthetic, the Duchess carefully preserved the character of the Grants' house, to the extent of retaining her grandfather's favourite chair in the drawing room and lovingly re-framing their family portraits – while introducing new comforts. The inevitable distress of Elizabeth Grant's later visit to her former family home was thus ameliorated by the Duchess's respect.

8.2: The Doune of Rothiemurchus from the 1911 edition of *Memoirs of a Highland Lady.*
By kind permission of the Scottish Record Office, Edinburgh.

It was to fall to her younger brother, Sir John Peter Grant, to rationalise the awkwardness of their father's partially completed house so that it might conform to High Victorian standards of propriety and comfort. He succeeded their brother, William, in 1874, and in 1878 called in the Edinburgh architect John Lessels (1808–1883). Although Lessels may be relatively unfamiliar (and has failed to attract the interest of a biographer), his 1869 design for St Leonard's in Edinburgh, in the shadow of Arthur's Seat, was immortalised by Ronald Searle's cartoons as the girls' school of St Trinians. It is now part of the University of Edinburgh's Pollock Hall.

Lessels was born into a family of clerks of works, who had been closely connected with the Fergusons of Raith for two generations. His first ambition had been to be an artist, and architecture was a practical, but second-best compromise. He remained an artist of some ability and sensitivity and, following his death, his extensive art collections, including his own studies of Roslin Chapel and many designs by earlier Scottish architects, were sold by Dowell's, the Edinburgh Fine art auctioneers in 1884. His son, also called John, went on to be Queen Victoria's clerk of works at Windsor Castle.

This preamble is necessary to fully appreciate the skill with which he transformed the Doune. Again, not only do none of his designs survive in the family muniments but, sadly, Lessels has left no office papers. His bill of quantities for his alterations to the Doune is marked 'design No.3'. There is every reason to think that the earlier, and presumably larger and more expensive designs, also nodded to Balmoral, and were in the Scotch Baronial style, then carrying all before it in the Highlands.

Architects had developed very considerable skills at transforming even essentially classical country houses like the Doune, into the desired asymmetrical and picturesque silhouette. Moy Hall, for example, was a neat classical box by John Adam, transmogrified into the required Scotch Baronial Castle. The Doune was doubtless to escape this fate purely on grounds of parsimony rather than merely taste.

The Lessels executed design, given that it was doubtless achieved without much money, was quite exceptionally clever even though it was in a now deeply unfashionable style. Lessels created the spacious new staircase and central hall, functioning as both circulation space and corridors, like the hub of a wheel, in the re-entrant angle between the Old and New Doune where it was best placed to resolve the historically diverse floor levels. Directly in front of this was the library, then still the Grant family's principal living room, although it must have lost its handsome fir bookcases during their financial vicissitudes. The new drawing room was given a capacious and fashionable Victorian bay window which, as in the other public rooms, had plate glass so that its view was unobstructed by glazing bars.

The smooth running of the house must have been eased through giving-up Elizabeth Grant's mother's first floor drawing room, which now became the 'Empress's Bedroom', with its adjoining dressing room. Over the new drawing room was the appropriately named 'Oriel Bedroom'. While the new staircase may seem to us to be Baronial in character, with its extensive run of massive ornamental woodwork, it was not out of keeping with the exterior late-Georgian character of the New Doune, whose thickening-up, as a result of the new-jamb, now made it look more substantial and convincing, and less like the wing of an incomplete house. Obviously, the continuance of the existing stripped-down Georgian style must have helped to contain costs, but a little ornamental relief was supplied, at moderate cost, by an ornamental cast iron cresting to the roof-line. The positioning of the staircase improved internal communications not only between the public rooms on the principal floor but also on the bedroom floor where communications between the Old and New Doune must always have been awkward. A columned portico was later added to the front door to underline the supremacy of the New Doune over the Old. The court of offices built by Elizabeth Grant's father was largely rebuilt to provide a kitchen and servants' bedrooms after the demolition of his original kitchen.

A series of photographs records Lessels' new interiors. Although Lessels introduced some modish and fashionable aesthetic details, principally to be seen in the carved wooden chimney-pieces, the existing late-Georgian character, even in the brand new drawing room, is rather remarkable and pre-figures the popularity of the Adam Revival. In 1878, the Adam Revival could otherwise only be found in the Highlands at Guisachan, whose owner, Lord Tweedmouth, was a pioneering collector of eighteenth century Wedgwood.

The character of these rooms is established by the chimney-pieces in the drawing room and dining room, the latter incorporating a landscape over-mantel. These surely must be old and genuinely Georgian rather than new and Adam Revival. Could these possibly also be from Thorley? Even with its over-mantle painting, the dining room chimney-piece is too small in scale for the enlarged room, suggesting that its re-use here may have had some deeper sentimental significance for the Grants. These pieces do not seem obviously Scottish. The dining room frieze has the freedom of John Adam's Georgian stucco work in houses like Arniston and Inveraray, but with its armorial shields suggests that it must be Victorian; the freedom of its modelling suggests the use of flexible gelatine moulds. It may be that the complexities of the plan of the dining room were the result of an enlargement involving the suppression of the kind of buffet-sideboard recess, beloved by the Scots, which may also explain why the existing chimney-piece ended up too small for the room. The drawing room frieze can only be described as Adam-Revival, and it is difficult to be certain about how it was achieved. Could it have been hand-painted, or by especially-printed paper?

Having given a new substance to the previously unresolved New Doune, Lessels' real stroke of genius was to lie in tricking-out the Old Doune so that it appeared to look convincingly like a much earlier tower-house, thus testifying visually to the family's ancient lineage. An extra storey was added, and a more elaborate silhouette was achieved with pepper-pot turrets to the gable-end. The entire composition was completed with a picturesque tower, which had the practical purpose of holding the water tank, lavatories and bathrooms. In the angle between the Old and New, a little knot-garden was created, overlooked by the new drawing room windows. What is rather moving is that these home improvements were followed by Elizabeth Grant, far away in Ireland, through the medium of photography. Never one to disguise her true feelings, she wrote to her brother: 'You have made a really pretty house of the former very odd-looking one'. She particularly admired the pepper-pot turrets as 'truly Scotch' and, although there had clearly been some uncertainty about the height of the new tower, she felt the end result looked satisfactory to her eye. A great deal of the credit for these successes must lie with Lessels.

A note of conviction was imparted to this rather theatrical Baronialisation by the incorporation of an earlier datestone – brought from another family property – which is why we did not begin this account with this trap set to historians of the Doune by this both very genuine as well as 'false' date.

It is possible that the rebuilt Doune, even after Lessels' improvements and Elizabeth Grant's own improvements at Baltiboys in Ireland, may reflect a nostalgia for their childhood home on the part of both brother and sister, which may have been shaped through their both having had to endure their different kinds of exile from their Rothiemurchus version of paradise before the family's fall.

If the Doune after Lessels' additions was rather more in keeping with standard Victorian country house conventions, as codified in such manuals as Robert Kerr's *The English Gentleman's House* (1864), it was now a much grander and more ambitious work of architecture, whose complicated roofworks and increased scale, demanded high standards of maintenance in the Highland climate. These demands, at a time of diminishing resources, were to see the Doune adapted to institutional use. The many Victorian bedrooms were ideal for both a hotel and a school (Gordonstoun was to be founded there), prior to the Second World War. Sadly, the Doune was not to enjoy sound building management in more recent years and thus decay and dry rot soon got the upper hand after the War.

The recent purpose of the restoration work has been to bring the Old Doune, whose smaller scale was best suited to the simpler way of life of the late twentieth century, back into domestic use as a self-contained family home. Timber, now ravaged by dry-rot, was pruned away. The concern was to remove as much of the timber that was directly in contact with damp masonry as possible, and it was replaced, as far as possible, by concrete and steelwork. After this drastic surgery, the old bones of the house re-emerged, with remarkably handsome results. If it is idiosyncratic, the Doune is certainly not as odd-looking as the Highland Lady had led us to think.

If we thus end back where we started with a view of the house before the Lessels' additions, this underlines the remarkable fact that such has been the vividness of her description of her father's house, that the power and force of her words have had the effect of returning the house nearer to its early nineteenth century appearance. At the time of writing the interior of the New Doune remains an empty shell, contrasting with the lived-in charm of the present Old Doune, but it seems at least highly likely that it will grow yet more like the house she describes, in the years to come, as it emerges into a new future as one of Scotland's most loved literary shrines.

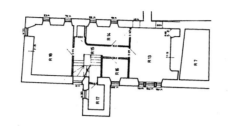

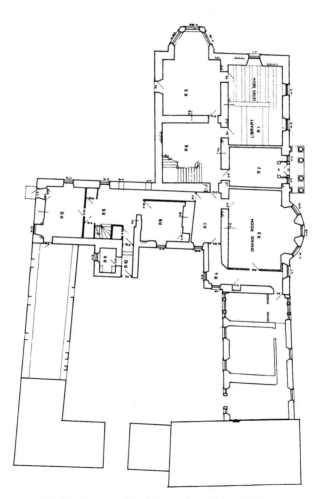

8.3: The Doune of Rothiemurchus, Ground Floor
Survey by Mary Tindall AADip RIBA RIAS in 1976
Photograph: by kind permission of Mary Tindall

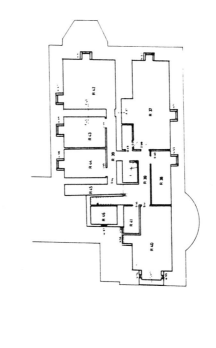

8.4: The Doune of Rothiemurchus, Upper Floor Plans
Survey by Mary Tindall in 1976
Photograph: by kind permission of Mary Tindall

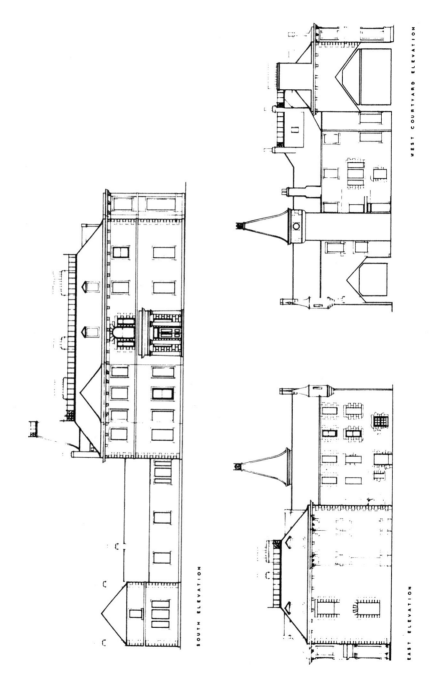

8.5: The Doune of Rothiemurchus, Survey Elevations
Survey by Mary Tindall in 1976
Photograph: by kind permission of Mary Tindall

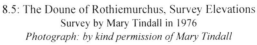

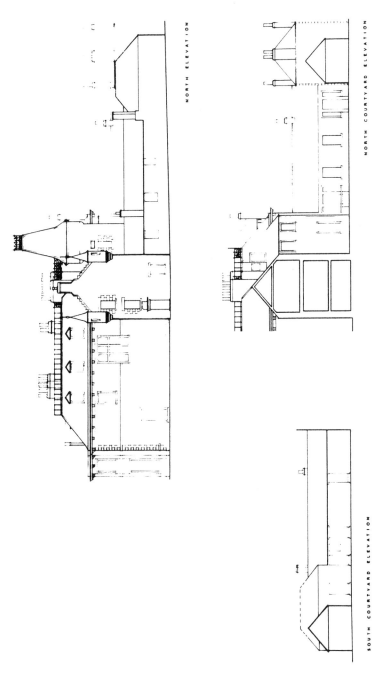

8.6: The Doune of Rothiemurchus, Survey Elevations and Section
Survey by Mary Tindall in 1976
Photograph: by kind permission of Mary Tindall

9. The Pleasures and Pitfalls of Editing the Works of the 'Highland Lady'

Andrew Tod

The 'Highland Lady', Elizabeth Grant of Rothiemurchus, was born two hundred years ago in her father's recently constructed New Town mansion at 5 Charlotte Square. Her long and busy life took her to Edinburgh, London, Oxford, India, the post-Waterloo Low Countries and France; much of her life from her marriage in 1829 to her death fifty-six years later she spent on the Co. Wicklow property of her husband, Colonel, later General, Henry Smith of Baltiboys, or in Dublin.

Throughout the majority of this long life she wrote the Journals for which her name is so justly remembered and on occasion, as David Calvert has outlined (see chapter 10), she wrote articles and short stories for some of the best known magazines of the day. She wrote most productively during the years 1840 to 1860. As she explained in one of her opening entries on 7 January 1840:

> It is for you, dear children, I am keeping this journal. I have often during my
> life done so before by starts .. and I have often regretted that I had not
> continued to do it. My experience of life, my love for you, all make me
> anxious to devote myself to your welfare, and if it should be God's will to
> take your parents from you, the voice of your mother 'from the grave' may be
> a guide and a protection.

There are several characteristic touches of the style associated with the 'Highland Lady' to be discerned here and they are of course those which make the life of an editor both easy and interesting, but this is a point I shall return to later. Necessarily, much has had to be omitted. The six hundred pages of the *Memoirs of a Highland Lady* are virtually every word she wrote in her manuscript, and the two hundred thousand words of the *Highland Lady in Ireland* represents perhaps a quarter of her complete diaries between 1840 and 1850.

In other words she wrote a great deal during these two productive decades. It is also worth reminding ourselves that these were written in the course of an extremely busy life. Her husband suffered from asthma and although he played his part in the life of the neighbourhood, for example, as a Poor Law Guardian, it is tempting to speculate whether he was not on occasion quite relieved to absent himself from the frenzy of activity at Baltiboys; one is reminded that the opening words of 1 January 1840 are '... a raw dark rainy day yet Hal out to look for the harriers.' From her journals it is clear that hers was the major part in the upbringing of their family, the routine organisation of the affairs of the estate and their role in a gregarious neighbourhood. And she found time busily to scribble down her thoughts most nights or when, less usually, she had a quiet spell during the day.

My involvement with her writings owes everything to three remarkable ladies and I would like to thank them for their help, co-operation and encouragement. First Moyra Fuller, the 'Highland Lady's' great-grand-daughter, through whom I was introduced to the, at that time, unpublished *Journals;* she produced, under her maiden name, Moyra McGusty, *The Irish Journals of Elizabeth Smith* in collaboration with David Thomson. When Canongate Press suggested an unexpurgated *Memoirs*, this was only made possible by the generosity of Ruth Frere, a great-great-grand-daughter, who readily lent her manuscript to the National Library of Scotland, where I spent many a weary but enjoyable hour having escaped from my place of more permanent employment to pursue what had become by now something rather more than a hobby. Thirdly another great-great-grand-daughter, my co-editor Patricia Pelly, with whom it has been such a pleasure to work and who has unstintingly allowed me access to all the Journals and papers of her distinguished ancestor; they are to be placed in the scholarly security of the National Library in Dublin so that there will be access for those who wish to pursue further researches.

This all made my editorial tasks much lighter but I think my greatest debt must be to Elizabeth Grant herself. She was an orderly and very well-organised lady whose working methods were a great help. Her handwriting is very easy to read and it flows effortlessly, and indeed economically, into each small corner of the pages she covers. She had, moreover, been well tutored with no less than seven masters being engaged for that dramatic winter of 1814/1815 when she experienced her broken romance ('It is with pain, the most extreme pain that I even now in my old age [she was *fifty*] revert to this unhappy passage of my youth'). Afterwards her father sensibly gave her various tasks to help him in his legal work:

> It may seem beyond the range of a girl of my then age to have entered into so grave a subject, but these sort of topicks were becoming my business. I wrote quickly and clearly, and seldom made mistakes; my father, though he had a Clerk, frequently found it suit him to employ me as his more private Secretary. I even helped him to correct the press for some of his pamphlets, sought out and marked his references, and could be trusted to make necessary notes.

Later, when she was recovering from the illness that prevented her from joining her family on the occasion of George IV's celebrated visit to Edinburgh in 1822, she spent a great deal of time pouring over 'the treasures of my father's library' at the Doune.

> First I took to light reading, but finding there allusions to subjects of graver import of which I was nearly ignorant, I chalked out for myself a plan of earnest study. The history of my own country, and all connected with it, in

eras, taking in a sketch of other countries, consulting the references where we had them, studying the literature of each period, comparing the past with the present. It was this course faithfully pursued till it interested me beyond measure that made me acquainted with the worth of our small collection of books. There was no subject on which sufficient information could not be got.

And, of course, all this was to stand her in good stead during that freezing last winter of 1826/1827 when she and her sister wrote those articles that were the family's only source of ready income ('Mary's papers were very clever, very original, they required condensing and a few grammatical corrections.')

If the implication is that hers required little correction to prepare them for *Fraser's Magazine*, the *Inspector* and the other utterly forgotten magazines they sent their offerings to, it might be worth recalling two occasions when she chose to close two of her chosen chapters, that for 1812 and for 1813, with words that also help to suggest she was in no doubt about her fitness to write about Rothiemurchus.

> Such was our highland home; objects of interest all around us, ourselves objects of attention all round, little princes and princesses in our *Duchus*, where the old feudal feelings get paraded in all their deep intensity. And the face of nature so beautiful ... the picturesque inhabitants, the legends of our race, fairy tales, the raids of the Clans, haunted spots, the cairns of the murdered – all and every thing that could touch the imagination, there abounded and acted as a charm on the children of the Chieftain who was so adored; for my father was the father of his people, loved for himself as well as for his name.

And she closes her chapter on the following year with a revealing comment on how she thought she and her siblings viewed this wonderful inheritance.

> There was never one highland feeling either in John or Mary. Jane in childhood was more taken up with the scenery than the people. William solely occupied with the idea of future power. All was to be some day his and that was sufficient to him. Little as they suspected it, I was the dreamer, could have been the Bard to the family as far as love for the race and a knowledge of their deeds could have qualified a candidate.

What, therefore, I think I am suggesting is that Elizabeth Grant was predestined to write, and that she was well equipped to tackle the tasks she had set herself.

There is an interesting beginning to her chapter on the years 1809/1810 which, for reasons of continuity, Lady Strachy chose to omit from the 1898 edition. It is dated Baltiboys, November 1845, so it was written four months after the Smith family's return after their two-year sojourn in France to be greeted by the ravages of the potato famine. She writes, very clearly, at the head of the chapter she has organised in her own mind for these years:

> Having got so far in these memorials of past life, the pleasure of the many half forgotten incidents now revived induces me to proceed in stringing together such recollections of our generation as can hardly fail, dear children, to be

interesting to you. The feebleness of my health at present confines me so
much to my room that I am neglecting nothing else while thus employing
myself, so ... on I go ... feeling that if any of you are like me, this history of
one of yourselves of the past age will be a curious family legend to refer to.

This is one of a number of occasions when she refers to her reasons for
committing herself to this, as it transpired, enormous project and I think the tasks
of an editor are helped to a considerable degree when there is a sort of
communion between, in this case she who is reminding herself occasionally why
so much is being committed to paper, and the later reader who might otherwise
struggle to make total sense of all that has been written.

One or two of these, from the as yet unpublished 1850s, seem to me to cast a
lot of light on her reasons for writing her Journal and the expectations she had of
the response of her family, but not necessarily those generations as yet unborn
who were to turn out to be her faithful readership and perhaps be tempted to
consider attending conferences based in part on her life and work. They also to
me represent much of the charm and interest of the opinions she expresses and
the language in which they are couched.

My fear for you, my dear Jack, is this; you are Irish and your father's son, and
so inherit a sort of desponding *give-up* disposition, the reverse of Bruce and
the spider, which with some indolence prevented your father rising to where
his abilities and his integrity would have placed him. In a degree this failing
has kept back his family – prevented his own usefulness. To educate you out
of this weakness, to give you the raven's never say die! must be my
unremitting care. Ask yourself when you read these words whether the poor
old mammy has succeeded; if not let her succeed *now* – it is never too late.
Mammy seldom lectured. Mind her when she does. [25 January 1854]

I thought for this week back that I would give up this journal. It grows dull on
my hands; age and troubles have cast a gloom over a once cheerful spirit and
the sameness of the life we lead is little calculated to revive it. But it was as
the loss of a friend to me; for so many years it has been my only intimate
companion, the repository of most of my thoughts, my feelings, my cares and
such pleasures as have crossed a chequered path, that the want of some such
safety valve seemed an evil. So here I am at the old egotostick work again. [8
January 1855]

I am almost inclined to burn all my old journals and never write another line. I
meant them to amuse my old age and to divert and to instruct my old age and
to instruct my children – disgust them probably, I fear, that is if they are at all
like the wretched, flippant, egotistical diary of the celebrated Miss Burney. I
never read such odious stuff. [23 January 1855]

I am just doubting whether it be worth while ever to set down any incidents in
my quiet life here; the life is so quiet, the incidents so few, the effect of them

on an old failing mind so uninteresting even to myself, to others useless. Who will wade through these sheets when I am gone. What would be found in them to repay the trouble. I sometimes think of burning the whole set of papers to save my heir the pain of doing it. When I was younger and busier and more alive, and when my General had real pleasure in having 'the journal' read to him weekly, then it was equal pleasure to me to write. It brought things to his mind which otherwise he might not have thought of. It educated me in the way of my duties. Now my work is done, my other self is gone; the young with their own aims are of a different era; I am all alone, and I really think the less I have to say to myself of myself the better. The indifference of old age has most certainly crept upon me; nothing is so acutely felt as it used to be, nothing makes the same impression. 'The tablet has hardened'; time for it to after seventy years. It bore many a deep cut in its softer day. [19 January 1865]

Editors are, of course, notoriously close to the writers they edit, but I hope that these four extracts provide without the need of any outside interference – heaven forfend that a footnote should interrupt the flow of her thoughts – evidence of the fascinating way her mind works, and that it is plain these are clear examples of the quality and value of what she wrote most days.

There are, of course, so many other examples that illustrate precisely why her writings are justly famed for the insights they provide into the world of Elizabeth Grant but they all have in common that they have been selected from a carefully written journal which it has been a pleasure and privilege to help to edit. It has been a pleasure, because although I am, like the Colonel, well aware of the infuriating side to her character, I rejoice at her intransigence, her broad mindedness, her intelligence ... and above all the ease with which I would suggest her thoughts can be extracted and presented to succeeding generations of appreciative readers. And of course it is a privilege, because I have been fortunate to help what I regard as an authentic voice of genuine quality from the last century to come to the attention of a wider public and thereby gain recognition as a unique contribution to our understanding of her times.

Let us remind ourselves of a few other examples from her published writings that support my contention. In any case, if I may return to one of my principal themes, they do not present many problems for an editor. Reviewers naturally spend the bulk of their copy on discussing the author, and the wretched hack who undertakes the editorial task tends to be dismissed in one of two adverbs; it has either been impeccably or wretchedly edited. I would challenge any rival editor to do much more than we have done. Paragraphing, punctuation and spelling are all I hope satisfactorily explained in the prefaces but these are merely tiny tinkerings to what she produced in order to enable her vivid and memorable prose to be more immediate to the modern reader.

Some of what she wrote about Sir Walter and Lady Scott, for example, in both the *Memoirs of a Highland Lady* and the *Irish Journals* only need to be set alongside, perhaps through footnotes, what can be gleaned from authoritative biographies; otherwise, as examples of contemporary and perhaps slightly unusual opinions, what she writes stands confidently on its own.

> I was never in company with Walter Scott; he went very little out and when he did go he was not agreeable, generally sitting very silent, looking dull and listless unless an occasional flash lighted up his heavy countenance. In his own house he was another character, especially if he liked his guests. His family were all inferiour. I have often thought that this was the reason of the insipidity of his ideal ladies and gentlemen – he knew none better.
>
> Poor Lady Scott, whom he only married out of pique, though probably he was not aware of it, was ever from the time I ever knew anything about her a most ridiculous little person, frivolous and stupid as far as a stranger could judge, without conversation, generally dressed an object, rouge and garlands of roses on a crop head when an old wrinkled woman and I should suppose incapable of bringing up her daughters, for they always flew about just as they liked, came to church in old bonnets and dirty frocks and without gloves, while she herself never came there at all.

The notorious visit of George IV to Edinburgh in 1822, stage-managed by Sir Walter, was another area where she was well aware that she had a good tale to tell and where she measured her words carefully to achieve maximum effect. It is worth reminding ourselves that she had a wider readership than her immediate family circle in mind as, for example, in June 1852 when she wrote: 'Goodnight my own dear Jack, for all this is for you – maybe you might find it a friend in need some day – sell it – have it revised and abridged or weeded – then publish like the rest of the world nowadays, and *fund the proceeds.*'

> One incident connected with this bustling time made me very cross. Lord Conyngham, the Chamberlain, was looking everywhere for pure *Glenlivet* whiskey – the King drank nothing else – it was not to be had out of the highlands. My father sent word to me, I was the Cellarer, to empty my pet bin, where was whiskey long in wood, long in uncorked bottles, mild as milk, and the true contraband *gout* in it. Much as I grudged this treasure it made our fortunes afterwards shewing on what trifles great events sometimes depend. The whiskey, and fifty brace of ptarmigan *all shot by one man in one day*, went up to Holyrood House, and were graciously received and made much of, and a reminder of this attention at a proper moment by the gentlemanly Chamberlain ensured to my father the Indian Judgeship.

It is in her *Irish Journals*, perhaps, that she rises from being a fascinating and well-written chronicler of her life and times to providing rock solid evidence seized on by historians of the 1840s to help contribute to their understanding of the effects of the potato famine in her part of County Wicklow. On 12 January 1847 she writes: 'Alas! the famine progresses; here it is in frightful reality to be seen in every face' and proceeds to describe how her daily routine is absorbed by her efforts to help those in need on the estate. There is a steely seriousness of purpose now about her writing.

> Who would exchange for this rational furthering of the improvement of our
> race, the life of the town lady? Or will any young woman brought up in this
> higher style of employment ever sink into the party giving idler?

As part of this campaign she determined to visit every cabin, hovel and improved
farm on Baltiboys so that she could prepare what she called 'a *catalogue
raisonné* of our population to leave among our family archives as a curiosity for
future squires and a guide to us now'. Here is an example of what she wrote
about a barely improved but coping tenant.

> Next farm ninety acres. Tom Kelly, an old man now, with old untidy ways;
> married at fifty, a girl with a hundred pounds who has made him an excellent
> wife. They have a large yard, new good offices, a garden, house of three large
> rooms, and seven children, four boys and three girls; plenty here but in an
> uncomfortable manner and the worst farming though the rent is never behind;
> no draining, no turnips, not sufficient stock. Hal means to resume about
> twenty acres of the low ground to reclaim himself as this stupid old creature
> can't be moved to exertion and we shall have a world of plague to get back the
> possession, both husband and wife acting tragedy when informed of it
> although they got this addition to their old holding on the express
> understanding of improving it.

Undoubtedly Baltiboys had been transformed in the seventeen years of the
Smiths' careful management and the long, regular entries in her Journal
effortlessly enable us to follow everybody on the estate and indeed the
neighbourhood at this terrible time. Every so often she manages, in the words of
the anonymous reviewer of *A Highland Lady in France* in the *Times Literary
Supplement* (7 March 1997), to 'transcend the prejudices of race and class', as
she attempts to generalise from what she has witnessed:

> It's nonsense to talk of good landlords as the rule; they are no such thing, they
> are only the exception. In my walks about this little locality have I not found
> evidence against them that would fit me for a witness before a Committee of
> the House of Commons, on the causes of Irish misery. When I pass the limits
> of our own ground, nothing meets me but misery.

This is a strikingly original and important observation and it was selected by Roy
Foster to illustrate the extent of the Irish famine in his magisterial *History of
Modern Ireland*.

The following extract from her published works is a whimsical but still
significant comparison she makes between the peasantry around Pau and those
with whose eccentric behaviour she was more familiar in Ireland.

> The peasants here should be no richer than with us, yet how much more
> comfortable they look. Too placid to take the least interest in anything beyond
> their immediate business, instead of flying about half mad in rags to make

mischief, they spend their quiet lives in habits of the strictest industry – the painter might prefer the wild bright eyed and rugged countenance, the thin, active figure, the rags and the tatters and the picturesque misery of the Irish cotter, but the philanthropist must dwell with far higher feeling on the comely features of the *Bearnais*, plump, contented, well-dressed, well fed, occupied. I have not seen a rag or tatter since I came, no men out at knees and elbows, no curious collection of bits hung together by some miracle as a covering ... The *Morning Herald* is perfectly right, what is most wanted in Ireland among all classes is the habit of industry – idleness is the mother of mischief indeed.

My final example, illustrating the ease with which such well-ordered, fascinating and eminently readable material can be edited into a shape that is absolutely true to the original and does not in any way confuse the modern reader, comes from the material. The 1850s are a splendid hunting ground for her prejudices as the Crimean War lumbers from disaster to eventual victory, as her son-in-law's financial problems become another major responsibility and her interest in all the social, political and religious developments of the day continue to merit, for the most part, outraged and indignant comments to her 'safety valve' of a diary. In July 1855 she was returning from a visit to Edinburgh where she visited Jack at the establishment where he was preparing for Sandhurst. She returned to Dublin by steamer and this extract comes from her description of what she saw on her journey.

A curious couple gave food for reflexion. An elderly fine gentleman, dressed young, airy, military, evidently in our own station, very conceited with careful dress, well trimmed hair and abundant moustaches, both deep red; his companion was a young pretty girl, many grades below him, merry and chatting but not forward, in dress and manner like a sempstress or other young person of a respectable industrial station, not smart enough for lady's maid. They were never apart a moment, they talked unceasingly, were on the most familiar terms, no tenderness in the manner of either, and she called him 'Sir'.

They met this morning close to me – 'How do? Sleep well?' said he. A laughing reply and counter question was answered by, 'Berth so confounded short!' He was not himself particularly tall. 'No room hardly to dress or anything – had any breakfast?' What she said I did not catch, but he resumed – 'Lord no, not my hours. Breakfast at eleven, dine at seven – how'll you like that, breakfast at eleven, dine at seven – eh! What do you say to that?' 'Let's go on deck' said she – 'It's stifling here' So up they went but soon came down again when he called for a biscuit and a glass of porter. When the bustle of landing began he collected all his traps in right soldierly fashion, he was quick and ready and had all neatly covered with oil cloth, his sword etc. On his head he placed a smoking cap with a long tassel like Hamlet's and then he went to help her with her poor carpet bag, her all of luggage. It was very odd, he did not seem uncomfortable, she was an innocent looking creature. They went off merrily together after the porter who carried their effects.

I think this is quite a good example of a well-structured anecdote which allows us to fill in the gaps in the narrative but there are a number of small points we concerned ourselves with that might help to illustrate our approach. Her spelling was retained so that 'reflexion' has an *x* and 'seamstress' lacks an *a* and has gained a *p*. The owner of the similar smoking cap was expunged as he was a gentleman friend from Dublin, Hamlet Thompson, who had yet to appear in her journal. But the main point was where to introduce a new paragraph and it seemed to us that the point of the anecdote for *her* became clearer if the opening paragraph ended 'and she called him sir'. This is a fairly straightforward instance but it might be worth repeating that such is the quality of her writing and her ever-present knowledge that what she was writing might well be read by posterity that the tasks of the editor are perhaps here better summed up in the French word *redacteur* – he or she who reduces.

I would like to end with the last words in her Journal, written in June 1885. They were perhaps her last written words, for she died shortly afterwards. She had at the end of her life returned to the Baltiboys she had helped to restore so many years before. I hope, and I do not believe that this is a fanciful comparison, that there might be an echo of Sir Walter Scott's final days at Abbotsford; after all, they are in the same league as diarists.

> Here I am again in the dear old room on the ground floor, the first I inhabited in the new house we were only building... I found all the things I ever used waiting for me – boxes, books, pictures, work-table, writing-table, chests of drawers, little ornaments, etc, etc, all here before me... I was escorted to bed by a suite like the Queen, candles in all hands and much laughter. So here I am, very, very comfortable, giving less trouble to the maids, indeed to everybody... It was just a little sad at first, old recollections would come back; I had been so happy here, and God be thanked, I am happy still, remembering the past fondly, and looking cheerfully forward for a space that won't be long.

Works of Elizabeth Grant in print

Memoirs of A Highland Lady. Elizabeth Grant of Rothiemurchus. Edited with an introduction by Andrew Tod. Canongate Classics, reprint 1997. ISBN 0-86241-3966.

The Highland Lady in Ireland. Elizabeth Grant of Rothiemurchus. Edited by Patricia Pelly and Andrew Tod. Introduction by Andrew Tod. Canongate Classics, reprint 1997. ISBN 0-86241-3613.

The Wicklow World of Elizabeth Smith, 1840-1850. Editors Dermot James and Séamas Ó Maitiú. The Woodfield Press, Dublin 1996. ISBN 0-9528453-O-X

A Highland Lady in France. Elizabeth Grant of Rothiemurchus. Edited by Patricia Pelly and Andrew Tod, with an introduction by Andrew Tod. Tuckwell Press, 1996. ISBN 1-898410-90-9

10. Elizabeth Grant and the Victorian Popular Press

David Calvert

Elizabeth Grant, the distinguished authoress and diarist of Scottish and Irish social history, was born in 1797, the eldest of the five talented children of Sir John Peter and Jane Grant of Rothiemurchus. There then followed William Patrick, born in 1798, who after a career in India greatly improved the forest management of his Rothiemurchus Estate; then Jane, born in 1800, a gifted artist; next Mary, born in 1803, briefly an authoress before her marriage, and lastly John Peter, born in 1807, who became a distinguished colonial administrator in India and Jamaica.[1]

The chronology of Elizabeth Grant's writings falls naturally into three parts, as shown in the diagram below:

Chronology of Elizabeth Grant's writing

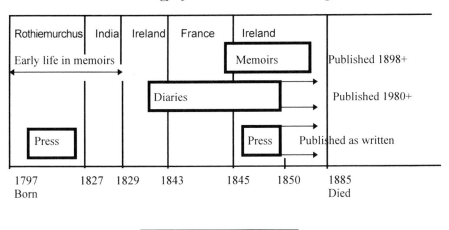

The memoirs, which allowed Elizabeth to 'live again her early years' were started on her birthday whilst she and her family were on holiday in France in 1845. They were written only for the interest and pleasure of her children, and they were only first published after her death, heavily edited by a niece, Lady Jane Strachey, in 1898 as *The Memoirs of a Highland Lady*. They became an instant success, and had to be reprinted three times in the first year. There is now a continuing interest in the expanded edition of the Memoirs.[2]

The diaries, which Elizabeth started in 1840 whilst living in Ireland, were continued throughout her long life, and have recently been partially published under the guidance of various editors such as Patricia Pelly and Andrew Tod (see chapter 9).[3]

The articles for the press, which were able to find a ready market in the expanding number of Journals and publications in the mid-nineteenth century[4] were, even at the time of publication, unrecognised as Elizabeth's writings – except by the editors – for she was published anonymously or only acknowledged as 'By a Lady' or as 'By the Author of My Father the Laird'. They remain undisclosed in the entry for Elizabeth Grant in *Chambers 1992 Scottish Biographical Dictionary*. To trace her publications thus requires some patience.

Elizabeth's earliest attempt at writing for the popular Victorian press occurred during the winter of 1825–6 when 'An Old Story', which she thought 'a lively little paper', was produced and submitted under a fictitious name to *Blackwoods*; sadly, the effort never received even an acknowledgement. The story was published later and provided Elizabeth with the sum of £3.[5]

It was partially to relieve the acute financial crisis which afflicted the family that Jane had married in December 1825,[6] just after her father had made suggestions for the liquidation of his debts,[7] and Elizabeth, for her part, was persuaded by a neighbour, Mrs Macpherson of Belleville, to recommence writing for the press.[8] During the summer and subsequent severe winter of 1826 Elizabeth and her sister Mary, working in the attic of their home at the Doune of Rothiemurchus, wrote several articles including Mary's 'The Country Campaign of a Man of Fashion', which gained favourable criticism in the *Times*, and her 'Matrimonial Campaign of a Man of Fashion'. For these literary efforts, most of which are at present unknown, the sisters received the sum of £40. This money was sufficient to provide previously unpaid wages for the two indoor servants, to provide for some shoes and necessaries, and to leave a small amount to be saved.[9]

An additional sum of £40 is mentioned for another packet of papers already printed, and for some which had been accepted for publication.[10] It is most probable that these packets contained 'The Painters Progress', in no fewer than eight parts. It was this second payment which provided essential support for the family on their journey from Rothiemurchus to Edinburgh, immediately before their voyage to India, for it enabled the carriage, which had been seized in Perth for a debt of £40, to be released and allowed their journey to Edinburgh to be completed.[11]

'The Painter's Progress' describes the travels of an artist who stayed at a Highland inn at which a wedding was about to be celebrated. After this wedding, a traveller crossing a swollen river was drowned, and so a Highland funeral is then described.

The story ends abruptly with the visit of the artist to a local laird, whose home and lifestyle are described. Elizabeth later explained that the story was less than half complete,[12] because the journal, *The Inspector, Literary Magazine and Review*, which ultimately became *The Inspector and National Magazine*, had ceased publication after a very short lifespan, suffering the fate of many similar Victorian publishing enterprises.

To put the remuneration received for Elizabeth's earliest writings in context, it is appropriate to compare these with other wages during the early nineteenth century. For example, William Chambers, who was later to publish much of Elizabeth's output, was engaged in 1814 as a bookseller's apprentice to Sutherlands in Carlton Street, Edinburgh, at 4 shillings per week – £10 per annum – for five years. His daily expenditure for food was three pence halfpenny, 1/9d per week (he walked home on Sundays), which with rent at 1/6d per week, left 9d per week for miscellaneous demands, mainly shoe leather.[13] Similar weekly wages – 3/- to 6/- – were paid to unmarried and married men respectively in Buckinghamshire in 1828, and only 4/- weekly for married farm labourers 'in nearby parishes'.[14] Elizabeth and her sister did realise that they had been rewarded with a small fortune, and the money was disbursed with considerable care.

After Elizabeth's own family returned to Ireland from their extended stay at Pau, and Avranches on the northern coast of France, extreme economic conditions again prevailed, this time caused by the Irish Famine. It was in order to support the school for the near destitute children from their estate at Baltiboys, set in the Wicklow foothills south-west of Dublin, that Elizabeth again took up writing as a source of income which she devoted mainly to this and other philanthropic projects.

This second period was one of considerable literary activity. Early in 1846 Elizabeth wrote three papers in quick succession, and was delighted at the pleasure she found in this renewed occupation: 'My Father the Laird', 'My Brother the Laird' and 'My Nephew the Laird', which were concerned with the fortunes under successive lairds of an entailed Highland estate set deep in a remote valley, were published in three successive editions of *Chambers' Edinburgh Journal*.[15]

A year later there appeared 'A Highlander of the last Age' which carried the sub-title 'By the Author of "My Father the Laird",' which reconstructed the early life of a retired Highland army officer from papers found in his home after his death. In these stories are many descriptions of the Scottish Highlands of Elizabeth's youth, intermingled no doubt with observations of her family and friends.

This literary output continued with a series of articles describing Elizabeth's experiences in France. 'Wintering in Pau' was a series of five papers which, although shortened by the editorial pencil,[16] added many background observations concerning French society to the day-to-day family events, which Elizabeth recorded in her diary during the period September 1843 to May 1844.

The holiday in June 1844, which the family spent in travelling near the Spanish frontier, formed the basis of 'A Month among the Pyrenees' and 'A Few Weeks at Cauterets among the Pyrenees'. These articles are extended accounts, albeit disguised, of the events recorded in the diary for that month.

10.1: 'I like my *Lairds* in print very well – to my amazement 'My Father' heads the paper.'
From *Highland Lady in Ireland*, 30 April, 1846.
By kind permission of University of St Andrews Library.

Elizabeth's acute observations of the condition of her own Irish estate and the behaviour of the local inhabitants are recorded in a set of four pieces with the general title *Mrs Wright's Conversations with her Irish Acquaintances*: 'The Good Match' describes the propitious engagement of Mrs Wright's niece to one who 'has no ready-made fortune, but possesses the means of making a fortune for himself'; 'Family Misfortunes' concerns the misadventure of a small boy who has been caught red-handed with some fir branches pulled from young trees on a plantation, and the subsequent revelation of the cause of the dire poverty of the boy and his family; 'Retrenchment' outlines the economies which will have to be achieved by a relative in order to remain solvent; and the fourth is an untitled conversation between a tenant farmer, his wife and Mrs Wright, discussing the improvements which could easily be achieved in local farming practice. These pieces exemplify a concern for tenants, and offer remedies for past errors which Elizabeth and her husband applied in the management of their own estate at Baltiboys.

The experiences which Elizabeth had in India provided the background to 'A Twelvemonth in Calcutta', a sixteen-part essay about the sojourn of a family in that city in the 1840s. Since there appears to be no evidence to suggest that Elizabeth was ever in Calcutta, it may be that this story has been created from detailed information supplied by correspondence with persons resident in Calcutta, possibly her parents.

The incomes which Elizabeth received from her writings provided essential succour on at least two occasions in her life: in Perth, to release the family carriage; and in the winter of 1848–49, when the £15 she received for the five 'Pau' papers – which she regarded as 'poor pay for there was a deal of work in them'[17] – kept her Irish household and farm solvent. In less stressful times, it enabled her to focus help to the children of the district through support for the school. In total, these additional monies may have added as much as 10% to the family income, and must have offered a welcome financial cushion on numerous occasions, and thus would have made all Elizabeth's literary efforts for the Victorian popular press worthwhile.

Once it is realised that, in addition to keeping her diary during the period August to December 1850, Elizabeth contributed some 50 densely printed pages to the 416 pages in volume 14 of *Chambers' Journal*, the magnitude of the output becomes apparent and it bears eloquent witness to the powers of observation, recollection and authorship which are her hallmark. That the effort was made largely in order to alleviate the poverty of local tenants and provide education for the children on the estate only increases one's admiration for this energetic and perceptive Highland Lady.

Notes

The abbreviations MHL1, MHL2 refer to *Memoirs of a Highland Lady* (edited A. Tod, Canongate Publishing, Edinburgh 1993) volumes 1 and 2.

The archives of the Grants of Rothiemurchus are catalogued in the Scottish Record Office, Edinburgh at NRA(S) 102. They are privately held at the Doune of Rothiemurchus, by Aviemore, Inverness-shire.

References

1. Walter Scott Seton-Karr, *Grant of Rothiemurchus - A Memoir of the Services of Sir John Peter Grant, GCMG, KCB* John Murray, London, 1899. Printed for private circulation.
2. John Letts, *The Sunday Times - Books*, 30 March 1997, page 7.
3. A bibliography of the editions of the works by Elizabeth Grant is given in *A Highland Lady in France*, edited by Patricia Pelly and Andrew Tod, Tuckwell Press, East Linton, 1996, page xvii.
4. Victor E. Neuburg, *Popular Literature, A History and Guide*, The Woburn Press, London, 1977. Chapter 4 1800-1897.
5. MHL2, page 196.
6. Elizabeth, MHL2, page 191, gives 20 December 1825 as the date of the marriage, whereas the Old Parish Registers, Inverness, Duthil and Rothiemurchus, chronicles 17 December 1825.
7. NRA(S) 102:356. 'Statement by J.P. Grant, Esq. of Rothiemurchus; and Proposal for the liquidation of his debts. Edinburgh, 8 March 1824'.
8. MHL2, page 195.
9. MHL2, pages 197,198.
10. MHL2, page 201.
11. MHL2, page 204.
12. *The Highland Lady in Ireland*, edited by Patricia Pelly and Andrew Tod, Canongate Classics, Edinburgh, 1991, page 544.
13. William Chambers, *Memoir of William and Robert Chambers*, W. & R. Chambers, Edinburgh, n.d. (post 1883), Chapter IV.
14. J.L. Hammond and Barbara Hammond, *The Village Labourer, 1760-1832*, Fraser Stewart Books, Abingdon, 1995, page 183.
15. NRA(S) 102:294 may contain manuscript versions of these stories.
16. *The Highland Lady in Ireland*, page 431.
17. *The Highland Lady in Ireland*, page 42

Acknowledgements

I wish to express my thanks to Robert Lambert for his support, to Christopher Smout and John Grant and their respective staff for organising the conference and visit to Rothiemurchus, to Norman Reid and the Library staff at St Andrews University for finding useful books, and to my family for their patience.

Lists of those works by Elizabeth and her sister Mary which have been traced, and those which remain undiscovered.

A. Articles written by Elizabeth Grant which have been traced in the *Inspector, Literary Magazine and Review*, which became the *Inspector and National Magazine* on 1 June 1827.

'The Painter's Progress'	Parts 1 and 2	3, 39-46, 1827	1 May 1827
	Parts 3 and 4	3, 139-146, 1827	1 June 1827
	Parts 5 and 6	3, 239-245, 1827	1 July 1827
	Parts 7 and 8	3, 537-543, 1827	1 Oct 1827

Mary Grant wrote, with Elizabeth's corrections, 'The Matrimonial Campaign of a man of
Fashion'   3, 432-440, 1827   1 Sept 1827

B. Articles written by Elizabeth Grant which have been traced in *Chambers' Edinburgh Journal, New Series.*

'My Father the Laird'		5, (119), 225-229, 1846	11 April 1846
'My Brother the Laird'		5, (120), 241-246, 1846	18 April 1846
'My Nephew the Laird'		5, (121), 261-264, 1846	25 April 1846
'A Highlander of the Last Age'		8, (198), 241-244, 1847	16 Oct 1847
(By the author of 'My Father the Laird')			
'Wintering in Pau'	Part 1	10, (244), 153-156, 1848	2 Sept 1848
(By a Lady)	Part 2	10, (246), 186-189, 1848	16 Sept 1848
	Part 3	10, (249), 236-239, 1848	7 Oct 1848
	Part 4	10, (253), 300-302, 1848	4 Nov 1848
	Part 5	10, (259), 396-399, 1848	16 Dec 1848
'A Month among the Pyrenees'		11, (287), 409-413, 1849	30 Jun 1849

'A Few Weeks at Cauterets, among the Pyrenees'

                                        12, (293), 93-95, 1849   11 Aug 1849

'Mrs Wright's Conversations with her Irish Acquaintances'
(This is believed to be the *second* set)

'The good Match'	14, (355), 251-252, 1850	19 Oct 1850
'Family misfortunes'	14, (356), 261-263, 1850	26 Oct 1850
'Retrenchment'	14, (360), 333-335, 1850	23 Nov 1850
Untitled	14, (364), 396-398, 1850	21 Dec 1850
'A Twelvemonth in Calcutta' Part 1	14, (344), 65-68, 1850	3 Aug 1850
Part 2	14, (345), 90-92, 1850	10 Aug 1850
Part 3	14, (347), 118-121,1850	24 Aug 1850
Part 4	14, (349), 152-155, 1850	7 Sept 1850
Part 5	14, (351), 184-187, 1850	21 Sept 1850
Part 6	14, (353), 210-213, 1850	5 Oct 1850
Part 7	14, (355), 246-249, 1850	19 Oct 1850
Part 8	14, (357), 285-288, 1850	2 Nov 1850
Part 9	14, (359), 314-316, 1850	16 Nov 1850
Part 10	14, (363), 381-383, 1850	14 Dec 1850
Part 11	15, (366), 11-13, 1851	4 Jan 1851
Part 12	15, (369), 60-63, 1851	25 Jan 1851
Part 13	15, (371), 93-95, 1851	8 Feb 1851
Part 14	15, (373), 125-128, 1851	22 Feb 1851
Part 15	15, (377), 189-191, 1851	22 Mar 1851
Part 16	15, (378), 200-203, 1851	29 Mar 1851

C. Articles which remain untraced, some of which may have been published, are:

i   Elizabeth's earliest articles, including 'An Old Story', which was published later.

Rothiemurchus

ii   Mary's 'Country Campaign of a man of Fashion', which is alluded to in her published article.

iii Elizabeth's pieces, including:

'Mr. Gray' : See *The Highland Lady in Ireland*, Edited by A. Tod & Patricia Pelly, Canongate Classics p 220, 29 March 1846.

'An Irish Sketch' : *ibid.*, p 229, 30 May 1846.

'A Highland Story' : may be a reference to 'A Highlander of the Last Age' *ibid.*, p 229, 30 May 1846.

'Thoughts on Irish Charities' was published in Howitt's *Journal of Literature and Popular* Progress : *ibid.*, p 341, 26 July 1847.

'National School' : *ibid.*, p 327, 15 May 1847 and p 351, 31 October 1847.

'Hannah White' may have earned Elizabeth £6.0.0d : *ibid.*, p 382, 26 April 1848.

'Luke White' : *ibid.*, p 345, 15 August 1847.

'Junior Clerk' provided Elizabeth with £2.0.0d : *ibid.*, p 481, 9 November 1849 p 500, 6 February 1850.

'Bordeaux' : *ibid.*, p 490, 9 January 1850.

'Clans' : *ibid.*, p 544, 29 December 1850.

Other parts of 'Mrs Wright's Conversations with her Irish Acquaintances'

Appendix 1

Entitled (in Gaelic)
'A song of sorrow about the Laird of Grant by James Grant, Laird of Rothiemurchus'

My great woe and nightmare
It caused my eyes to shed tears;
It caused injury to my heart
Which cannot be diagnosed by a physician,
The news which was heard about the Laird of Grant.

Rightful chief of the Strathspeymen
Noble, honourable, handsome.
Wise, courageous, gallant,
You were respected above hundreds
In the courthouse and you were useful in war.

Teeth as evenly shaped as dice,
An eloquent mouth to expostulate the truth,
To support your kindred
And to chastise those of ill-will,
Sore is the dart under my breast for I sadly miss you.

The Duke of Argyll and the Duke of Gordon
Are in sadness over you;
That is little wonder for them,
Bulwark of battle are you who would not yield
You have left your own great clan in a state of grief.

My great loss that you are in England
With the hue of illness upon you
And the tower of Castle Grant
And the *dùthchas* of your clan
Are without your presence, widowed.

I have seen, although I am young,
Many a feast in that large house,
Many young men and maidens,
Noble, modest, merry
And they joyfully, musically dancing.

When your beautiful banner would be unfurled,
There's many a champion and warrior
Who could fearlessly march
Who would be in battle order about your gate,
When they would perceive the flame of the chiefs.

Men of the powder flasks
And of the muskets with barrels of dark blue
And of the slender swords.
There would be pistols with new firelocks
And embossed targes with closely set studs on every one of them.

These things were their boast since they came into existence:
To go with the order of the chief
Into the torment of swordplay,
Without faint-heartedness or fear
And without hope of returning without suffering great hardship.

There's many a valiant young warrior
Comely in kilt
And skilful with targe
Who would quickly answer your call,
Who is in sorrow over you at this present time

Oh God who created the garden
Out of which the heroes arose
Who made fruit and blossom grow in it,
Look down on us and through your grace,
Send up to us, in our distress, our chief.

(Reproduced by courtesy of James Grant, Dept. of Celtic, University of Aberdeen)

Appendix 2

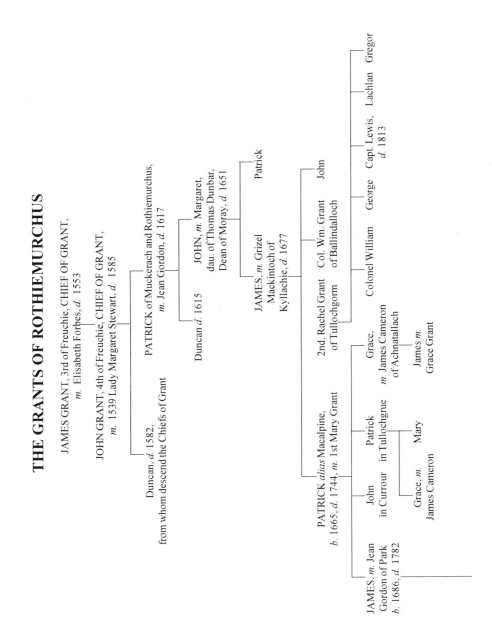

THE GRANTS OF ROTHIEMURCHUS

JAMES GRANT, 3rd of Freuchie, CHIEF OF GRANT, *m.* Elisabeth Forbes, *d.* 1553

JOHN GRANT, 4th of Freuchie, CHIEF OF GRANT. *m.* 1539 Lady Margaret Stewart, *d.* 1585

Duncan, *d.* 1582, from whom descend the Chiefs of Grant

PATRICK of Muckerach and Rothiemurchus, *m.* Jean Gordon, *d.* 1617

Duncan *d.* 1615

JOHN, *m.* Margaret, dau. of Thomas Dunbar, Dean of Moray, *d.* 1651

Patrick

JAMES, *m.* Grizel Mackintoch of Kyllachie, *d.* 1677

2nd. Rachel Grant of Tullochgorm

Col. Wm. Grant of Ballindalloch

John

PATRICK *alias* Macalpine, *b.* 1665, *d.* 1744; *m.* 1st Mary Grant

John in Currour

Patrick in Tullochgrue

Grace, *m.* James Cameron of Achnatallach

Colonel William

George

Capt. Lewis, *d.* 1813

Lachlan

Gregor

Grace, *m.* James Cameron

Mary

James *m.* Grace Grant

JAMES, *m.* Jean Gordon of Park *b.* 1686, *d.* 1782

PATRICK, m. Helen Grant, d. 1790, s.p.

William M.D. m. Elizabeth Raper, d. 1786

George

The Rev. Alexander, m. Diana Neale

Helen m. Alex. Cumming of Logie, and had issue

Henrietta m. Patrick Grant of Glenmoriston, and had issue

Elizabeth Raper, m. George Frere

Sir JOHN PETER, b. 1774, m. Jane Ironside, d. 1848

John, m. Jane Dalton, and had issue.

George. m. Margaret Corrie, and had issue

Bartle, m. Adelaide Rowe, and had issue

Elizabeth d. unmarried

Susan, m. Christopher Wordsworth, Bishop of Lincoln, and had issue

Anne, m. Capt. John Ed. Frere. R.N., and had issue

Judith, m. Charles Merivale, Dean of Ely, and had issue

WILLIAM PATRICK, b. 1798, m. Sarah Siddons, d. 1874, s.p.

Sir JOHN PETER, G.C.M.G., K.C.B., b. 1807, m. Henrietta Chichele Plowden, d. 1893

Elizabeth, b. 1797, m. General Hy. Smith, 'THE HIGHLAND LADY', d. 1885

Jane, b. 1800. m. 1st Col. Gervase Pennington; 2nd, James Gibson Craig, d. 1863. s.p.

Mary Frances, b. 1804, m. Thomas George Gardiner, d. 1844

John Grayden, m. Fanny Harvey, and had issue, d. 1873

Jane, m. George Richey, and has issue

Anne, m. James King, and has issue

Thomas George. m. Mary Georgina Katharine Barnard, and has issue

John Peter, d. 1857

Jane. m. Geo. Gordon Mackintosh

JOHN PETER, b. 1836, m. Marion Rowe, d. 1893

Trevor John Chichele, m. Clementina Gouldsbury, and has issue

George Francis Mytton. m. Isabel Gore-Singleton, and has issue

Charles m. Agnes Isaacs, and has issue

Bartle, m. Ethel MacNeil and has issue

Frances Elinor m. The Rt. Hon. Sir James Colville

Jane Maria, m. Lieut-General Sir Richard Strachey, G.C.S.I., and has issue

Henrietta Anne

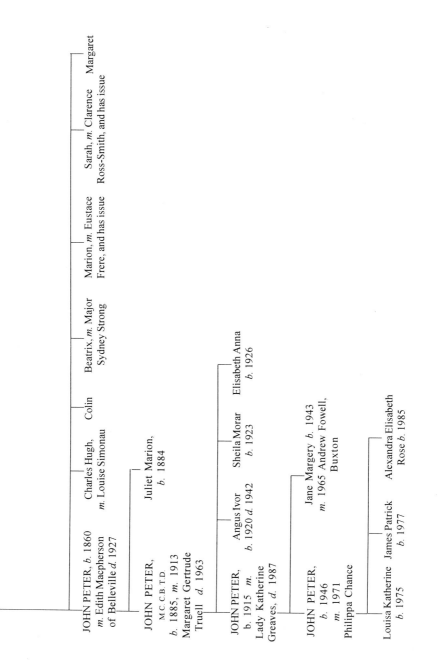

INDEX